DATA FOR DIGNITY

DATA FOR DIGNITY

LEVERAGING TECHNOLOGY IN THE FIGHT AGAINST HUMAN TRAFFICKING

MELISSA BIRCHFIELD

NEW DEGREE PRESS

DATA FOR DIGNITY

Leveraging Technology in the Fight against Human Trafficking

ISBN   978-1-64137-354-8   *Paperback*

         978-1-64137-688-4   *Ebook*

*For all those trapped in slavery today, whose
lives I have touched without knowing it.*

CONTENTS

Freedom is a delicate gift, easily distorted and often squandered.

Freedom is so easily overlooked, so easy to forget about until you no longer have it.

I remind my heart and mind that we have this freedom not to abuse... but to leverage.

—KELLY WELK, FOUNDER OF FREEDOM

DINNERS AT CIDERPRESS LANE

INTRODUCTION

———

Liz Rush had never seen a drearier January.

A few years back, she had decided to enroll in an intense programming academy after college... and had discovered that she loved it. From debugging lines of code to optimizing system performance, she found the Seattle tech startup scene exciting, a fast-paced environment that kept her on her toes.

But that's not what kindled her passion.

Her heart kept pulling her toward the plight of women, men, and children who were trapped in exploitation. As she had volunteered in domestic violence shelters ever since she was a teenager, she'd become acquainted with countless forms of victimization. She knew that slavery wasn't a scourge of the past. Every day—in Seattle, across the United States, and around the globe—millions of individuals toiled without dignity or hope of escape.

**

In a time when technology is rapidly spreading into every corner of our lives, the problem of human trafficking and modern-day slavery also looms larger than ever. As of 2016, the Global Slavery Index estimated that there are 40.3 million people enslaved worldwide—but statistics are uncertain due to the difficulty of identifying victims as well as discrepancies in definitions of exploitative crimes.[1] Regardless, the issue is impossible to ignore. Even one individual in slavery is an unacceptable violation of human dignity.

Human trafficking includes any use of force, fraud, or coercion to extract commercial value from another person. In the United States, we divide human trafficking into two legal categories: labor trafficking and sex trafficking.[2] This distinction is often a muddy one, however, as sexual abuses are not uncommon in situations of forced labor and vice versa. Globally, labor trafficking claims more victims than sex trafficking, with individuals lured by the promise of opportunity into a job from which they are unable to escape— their traffickers keep them in perpetual debt, threaten to harm their families if they defy authority, confiscate their

---

1   "2018 Findings: Executive Summary." *Global Slavery Index*, 2018. The Walk Free Foundation (September 28, 2019).

2   "Fact Sheet: Human Trafficking." *Office on Trafficking in Persons*, November 21, 2017. U.S. Department of Health & Human Services (September 28, 2019).

passports, or transport them to unknown locations so that they remain alone and confused.

Too often, our society frames human trafficking as a third-world country issue that has little to no relevance in our daily lives. Many of us don't even know that modern-day slavery exists, or if we are aware, we brush it aside as "not our problem." The reality is, our globalized world is built on the backs of slave labor, with an increasingly intricate supply chain making it ever more difficult to trace the origins of our products. From our clothes to our chocolate, from our makeup to our mobile phones, we all have a "slavery footprint" whether we're conscious of it or not. And it's not only happening overseas.

There are more victims in our hometowns than we'd like to admit, but we don't notice because we aren't looking for them.

It's hidden in plain sight.

The more ignorant we are, the more it festers unhindered.

But once you know, you can't *not* do something.

**

Liz stared at her computer screen, trying to focus. She was finding less and less personal fulfillment in software development. "Programming can be cool, but it [often] doesn't really make the world a better place," she told me after we met at an anti-trafficking fundraiser.

Eventually, she decided to duck out of her startup in order to pour her time into volunteering for a victim support team with the Seattle Police Department. That was where her true passion lay: supporting survivors of domestic violence, sexual exploitation, and human trafficking as they broke free of abuse and began to take control of their own lives.

At the time, the tech world seemed deplorably insular, a distraction from meaningful work. Yet in the back of Liz's mind, the possibility was sprouting:

What if she could bring her technical skills *into* the anti-trafficking realm?

What if, instead of a frivolity, technology could be honed into a formidable weapon to disrupt the patterns that allow slavery to persist?

**

A year ago, I was unaware that these horrific injustices were unfolding around me. Human trafficking was something that no one had ever talked about with me, and frankly, it was a topic that I avoided bringing up on my own. Although vaguely cognizant that many people lived in degrading and exploitative conditions, I assumed that it all happened far away in developing countries. Surely, there was nothing that I could really do about it. I avoided asking questions because I was scared of what the answers would be.

All that changed during my third quarter in college, when I enrolled in an honors course at the University of Washington dedicated to "Understanding and Combating Human Trafficking." Suddenly, I found myself plunged into a new perspective where my previous misconceptions flew out the window, replaced by a sobering—and overwhelmingly nuanced—picture of slavery today. It was no longer a vague notion somewhere over the ocean, across the border. It was in my trip to the store. In the woman across the street. In the man on his phone.

As an emerging technologist trying to figure out what I wanted to do with my computer science degree, I set out to see if there was a way that I could get involved in anti-trafficking work. What I found surprised me on many fronts.

On the one hand, I realized that we frankly don't have much figured out in terms of eradicating slavery. It's woven itself into the fabric of our globalized society, in many ways facilitated by technology, lurking in cultural and political systems, thriving in a world where most of us are more or less oblivious, and those few individuals who *are* trying to fight it often end up flailing in a graveyard of disconnected, misdirected efforts.

At the same time, I can't help but be excited about the future. As I talked with people—software engineers, lawyers, directors of non-profit organizations, and survivors themselves—who have spent years working to eradicate human trafficking, I've been inspired by their relentless commitment to this cause. From identifying current victims, to supporting survivors as they forge a new life, to designing strategies for preventing slavery in the first place, they have shared with me the ways that their technology is making an impact on the ground, as well as their visions for the future.

In these chapters, you'll delve into incredible stories from individuals who followed their own calling into this space, and the remarkable technologies they're imagining for a slavery-free future. You'll discover…

- How Liz Rush found a way to spearhead a software platform that reaches out to individuals trapped in the sex trade.
- How a team of researchers and volunteers trained machine learning algorithms to track slavery from space.
- How a tiny device the size of a smartphone is changing the tide for forced labor on fishing vessels in Southeast Asia.
- How a chatbot has made strides in deterring men from buying sex from trafficking victims.
- How two friends created a coding academy to transform female survivors into software professionals.
- And much more…

You'll learn about the successes they've embraced and the hard lessons they've had to grapple with along the way. But you'll also hear why they continue to pursue their work and why they're ultimately hopeful about the future, just as I am.

**

If you're still trying to figure out what to do with your career, wanting to make the most of your skills while working on something meaningful, this book is for you. If you've ever chewed on the mantra, "Make the world a better place," and wondered what that actually looks like, this book will share the paths of people who are doing just that. Whether you know nothing about human trafficking or it's already on your heart, whether you're a technologist or simply a user of technology, whether you have just a few minutes a day or if you're wanting to change your entire trajectory, my hope is that you'll be both challenged and inspired. That you'll see the problem but also the tremendous possibilities ahead.

Believe me, there's a role for you to play.

Much has been done—yet there is so much to be done.

While it's a daunting mission, it's also an invigorating one—and here's the most exciting part: no matter what field you're in, no matter what expertise you have, *you can make a difference.* You can join the fight.

What's going to get us there? First of all, an *awareness* of the myriad shades of slavery lurking right beneath our noses and the *indignation* that won't let us stand by idle. Together, these spark the *passion* that propels us into the fight for freedom, far and near. In order to tackle the problem head-on, we'll need *creativity* to examine the status quo from unconventional angles, angles that we must approach with the getting-your-hands-dirty sort of *humility*. We'll need to connect across disciplines to design and implement multi-faceted solutions, honing our efforts in close-knit *collaboration*. We've got to maximize our time, resources, and brainpower. And we'll need *perseverance* to maintain a tenacious perspective as we push through setbacks along the way.

When it comes to leveraging technology against modern-day slavery, I believe I've only peered into the depths of the potential that's waiting for us. Collectively, we've merely scratched the surface. There's so much more to explore, so many ways that we can wield technology to rally together for real change.

Come join me on this journey to uncover a cause that desperately needs to be in the spotlight.

PART 1:

LAYING THE GROUNDWORK

"Why not show up for even one—the way you wish someone would show up if it were you?"

—ANN VOSKAMP

CHAPTER 1:

WHAT IS HUMAN TRAFFICKING?

———

"Men and women have the right to live their lives and raise their children in dignity, free from hunger and from the fear of violence, oppression or injustice."

—MILLENNIUM DECLARATION, SEPTEMBER 2000[3]

Before we plunge into any effort to eradicate human trafficking, it's of utmost importance to understand the problem we're trying to tackle. Far too many precious resources have been wasted, and far too much energy has been channeled in ineffective directions, simply because people have not

3   "Millenium Declaration." un.org, September 2000. United Nations (September 28, 2019).

comprehended the scope of human trafficking or the complexities surrounding it. With so many myths and misconceptions around the issue, it's worth the time to dispel them upfront.

When I asked students at my university what comes to mind when they hear the term "human trafficking," their answers reflected the way that the media has romanticized and distorted the issue: Women gagged and bound in chains. Children kidnapped out of the blue. Girls auctioned off on sketchy websites. It's been framed as a women's issue, as a third-world country issue, and as an immigration border control issue. No matter which way it's painted, it usually ends up as "not my problem"—the skeleton in our closet that we suppress without realizing it.

In reality, the monster of modern-day slavery takes many forms, and the first step toward eradicating it is recognizing it for what it is.

HUMAN TRAFFICKING DEFINED

December 2000 marked a new global attitude toward human trafficking, inflamed by the United Nations Convention against Transnational Organized Crime in Palermo, Italy. Kofi Annan, who was Secretary-General of the United Nations at the time, referred to the Convention as a "watershed event in the reinforcement of our fight against organized crime."[4] The resulting "Palermo Protocol" heightened our

---

4   "United Nations Convention against Transnational Organized Crime and the Protocols Thereto." *United Nations Office on Drugs*

understanding that, given the transnational nature of human trafficking, we must combat it on a similar scale. Our efforts should not be confined within each country but rather coordinated for comprehensive action.

Since the adoption of this "Palermo Protocol," many countries have amplified their efforts to identify and counter modern-day slavery. In the United States, for instance, the Trafficking Victims Protection Act of 2000 (TVPA) appeared around the same time, providing legal provisions for survivors to support them on their journey toward justice and healing. The TVPA lays out a definition of human trafficking categorized into either labor or sex trafficking, involving "the recruitment, harboring, transportation, provision, or obtaining of a person" for commercial sex acts or some kind of forced labor induced by force, fraud, or coercion.[5]

Under these definitions, a person does not have to be physically bound under lock and key, nor procedurally bought or sold, in order to be considered a victim of human trafficking. Also, he/she does not necessarily have to be moved from one place to another, which is one reason why many countries commonly use the term "modern slavery" rather than "human trafficking." (In the United States there's more sensitivity around the word "slavery" because of its

and Crime, 2004. United Nations (September 28, 2019).

5   "One Hundred Sixth Congress of the United States of America at the Second Session." *Gov Info*, January 24, 2000. U.S. Government Publishing Office (September 28, 2019).

centuries-old association with the systemic enslavement of African-Americans.) For the most part, in this book I will use these terms interchangeably, in particular taking cues from the language used by different organizations and individuals as they're presented.

While certain groups of people are more vulnerable than others, *anyone* can be a victim of human trafficking. And *anyone* can be a trafficker—man or woman, wealthy or poor, marginalized or well-respected. This often makes it difficult to recognize situations that would be classified as human trafficking. However, the exercise of force, fraud, or coercion creates a common thread through the myriad forms of slavery, as at least one of the three elements must be present in order for a situation to be legally considered a case of human trafficking. Let's take a closer look at these criteria outlined by the TVPA:

Force may be the closest to what people tend to imagine with regards to how traffickers control their victims. Through kidnapping, beating, rape, torture, seizing a phone or a passport, moving someone from one place to another, locking them in a room, etc., traffickers isolate their victims to maintain control over their activity and their ability to communicate with others.

Fraud includes any form of deception used to recruit victims or to keep them from leaving. For example, a couple in India could agree to work in a brick kiln to pay for their sick child's medical bills, ending up in debt bondage with an unknown amount that they are never able to repay. Or a foreign recruiter could lure someone into a promising job opportunity, only to confiscate their papers and force them to work in conditions much more degrading than they'd expected to pay off their travel expenses—a debt which, again, only increases over time. Sometimes these victims will work for legitimate companies, like a fast food restaurant or a nail salon, with their employers hardly suspecting that their paycheck is being siphoned off into someone else's pockets.

Coercion involves a degree of psychological manipulation that prevents victims from escaping, even if they are not physically trapped. Often, traffickers will threaten to harm the victims' families back home if they try to escape. Other times, they'll convince victims (sometimes rightfully) that they have nowhere to turn to for help—they would be arrested for prostitution, petty theft, drug use, or their illegal immigrant status. After undergoing so much psychological trauma, many victims are unable to even imagine a life of freedom. They might feel so much shame that they wouldn't dare return home, or they could be bound by a twisted dependence to their trafficker, especially if that person is a "boyfriend" or a family member.

WHERE YOU LEAST EXPECT IT

The unsettling reality about human trafficking is that it can happen to *anyone.*

My honors professor, Dr. Foot, told my class a story that hit close to home. Her neighbor routinely stopped at a small coffee drive-through in the mornings, gradually finding it odd that the girl who took her order looked young enough to be a high school student. When the neighbor finally asked why she wasn't in school, the girl responded that she was working to pay off her debts to her aunt and uncle. They had offered to let her stay with them if she left her hometown in Central America, but before she could begin her education in the United States, they'd told her that she needed to pay them back for her travel expenses. She had never seen any of the money she earned and had no idea when her debts would be fully paid. She also didn't realize that she was a victim of labor trafficking.

In August 2019, the FBI conducted a month-long sex trafficking sweep across the United States, working with over 400 law enforcement agencies in fifty-six cities on sixty different federal investigations. KOMO News reports that "undercover officers scanned social media and escort sites looking for what appeared to be juveniles advertising for commercial sex."[6] Once they contacted these individuals, they arranged fake dates that turned into interviews to gather more information that would help them verify if these were underage trafficking victims, and if so, take action. As a result of this sweep, the FBI identified 103 juvenile survivors and arrested 67 suspected traffickers. Las Vegas had the highest number of rescues (14), followed by

---

6   "Six teens rescued during FBI sex trafficking sweep in Seattle." *Komo News*, August 7, 2019. Sinclair Broadcast Group (September 28, 2019).

Dallas (13), and Detroit (9). My current home city, Seattle, tied with Atlanta for the fourth-highest place, with six teens rescued.

In the same month, news stations across the United States reported about Lavon Franz, a newspaper carrier in Des Moines, Iowa, who stopped during her morning route for a woman who was crying and waving her arms at her from the roadside.[7] The woman told her that she wanted to go back home after a "bad breakup" with her boyfriend, but she had no cellphone or ID. Franz knew instinctively that something wasn't right. She drove the woman to a nearby convenience store. The clerk called the police, and they found that the woman had been sold for sex at local hotels. Her trafficker? A 25-year-old woman named Brittany Walters who arranged the "dates" for this woman as well as at least three other victims.

Across the Atlantic, labor trafficking occurs in one sector you probably haven't considered: car washing. This is a problem especially in the United Kingdom, where up to 20,000 hand car washes (HCWs) can be found on the side of the road, in supermarket parking lots, and at gas stations. Akilah Jardine, a research fellow at the University of Nottingham's Rights Lab, notes that "such labor-intensive operations are fueled largely by an abundant, low-skilled

---

7   Gehr, Danielle. "Newspaper carrier picked up sex-trafficking victim, leading to Illinois woman's arrest." *Des Moines Register*, August 2, 2019. Des Moines Register (September 28, 2019).

workforce."[8] Unfortunately, this fragmented, little-regulated employment sector lends itself to exploitative practices and modern slavery. "Reports suggest that HCW workers work excessive hours, are paid below the national minimum wage and operate in poor living and working conditions," writes Jardine.[9] For instance, police have interacted with employees who were trafficked from Romania and forced to work in the car washes, where they scoured the cars for stray coins in order to stay alive. However, public acceptance of cheap services often leads to a "no questions asked" mentality. Most people are unwilling to dig deeper into these employees' well-being beyond the superficial work they provide.

I could retell story upon story...

A ten-year-old indigenous girl in Mexico was sold by her mother to a family who, instead of helping her attend school, forced her to become full-time caretaker and housekeeper, in animal-like conditions, for nearly thirty years.[10]

---

8   Jardine, Akilah. "Labour Exploitation in the UK's Hand Car Wash Sector." *Delta 8.7*, August 14, 2019. United Nations University Centre for Policy Research to Alliance 8.7 (September 28, 2019).

9   Ibid.

10   Romo, Rafael. "Thirty years living and working as a modern-day slave." *The CNN Freedom Project*, April 28, 2017. CNN (September 28, 2019).

A Canadian girl was introduced by an older "friend" to crack cocaine and then recruited into sex work when she was eleven years old.[11]

A young woman from southern Nigeria migrated to Paris to be a waitress, only to find out that she'd been lured into a sex trafficking network via a ritual-heavy "juju" oath to repay her debt to her madam pimp and never speak of it to anyone—a powerful form of coercion, which terrified her and thousands of other girls into believing that they would go insane or die if they broke it.[12]

Twelve men from Bangladesh were enslaved at a hotel in Scotland, coerced into paying back their visa fees by performing much more than the chef work they had agreed to do.[13]

Children in Ghana are forced to work on fishing boats, their small size and nimbleness necessary for such tasks as removing fish from the nets and disentangling nets from the bottom of Lake Volta.[14]

Children in Kenya are recruited into orphanages—even if they have guardians who would take care of them—with

11 "Survivor overcomes her sex trafficking past." *The CNN Freedom Project*, 2017. CNN (September 28, 2019).

12 Andrews, Frank. "The Paris park where Nigerian women and forced into prostitution." *The CNN Freedom Project*, October 5, 2018. CNN (September 28, 2019).

13 Soares, Isa. "These men were forced into slavery in Scotland." *The CNN Freedom Project*, 2017. CNN (September 28, 2019).

14 Johansen, Raggie. "Child trafficking in Ghana." *UNODC*, 2019, United Nations Office on Drugs and Crime (September 28, 2019).

the promise that they'll be given better food, shelter, and education than their family members could provide. However, their presence is exploited to convince well-meaning donors and tourists to gifts funds to the "orphanage"...funds that are never used to actually benefit the children.[15]

Will there ever be an end?

Often it seems that the more closely we look for human trafficking, we begin to see it everywhere. And yet, it's so important to understand the scope of the problem in order to tackle it most effectively.

HOW MANY VICTIMS?

It would be overwhelming to describe every possible scenario of human trafficking, but if nothing else, I hope it's clear that these cases are incredibly nuanced and usually very different from the sensationalized media representation of a conspiratorial network of evil. Beyond the more common examples of labor and sex trafficking, other manifestations of slavery include child soldiers, forced brides, organ trafficking, and "orphans" given up for adoption or used to attract funds from unsuspecting donors. For the traffickers, it's all about money. Low risk, high reward. It's one of the most lucrative criminal enterprises in the world—according to a 2014 report by the International Labour Organization, human trafficking generates about

---

15 "Orphanage 'recruited kids to get donations'." *The CNN Freedom Project*, March 8, 2017. CNN (September 28, 2019).

$150 billion in profits each year—and it's claimed the freedom of millions of individuals.[16]

How many millions? That's difficult to say, given the varying opinions of what should be considered a human trafficking situation. If we aren't looking for certain scenarios, we won't find them. When we do undertake the task of tallying numbers, there arises the question: Who counts as a victim? Often, victims themselves don't self-identify, unable to recognize their situation for what it is. And their traffickers certainly don't want others finding out about the individuals within their control. Out of the cases that do come to light, few are brought to court and even fewer are actually prosecuted as trafficking cases because of how hard it can be to prove the presence of force, fraud, or coercion.

As far as numbers go, a 2017 report by the International Labour Organization (ILO)—in partnership with the Walk Free Foundation (creator of the Global Slavery Index) and the International Organization for Migration (IOM)—estimated that there were 40.3 million victims of modern-day slavery worldwide in 2016.[17] This includes victims of labor and sex trafficking as well as forced marriages. Women and girls accounted for seventy-one percent of all victims and

---

16 "ILO says forced labour generates annual profits of US$ 150 billion." *ILO*, May 20, 2014. International Labour Organization (September 28, 2019).

17 "Global Estimates of Modern Slavery. *International Labour Office*, 2017. International Labour Organization, Walk Free Foundation, and International Organization for Migration (September 28, 2019).

ninety-nine percent of forced commercial sex workers. One in four victims of modern slavery were children. For more detail, the Global Slavery Index provides a country-by-country breakdown of the ways that each government is responding to the issue.[18]

Besides the Global Slavery Index, another resource for understanding human trafficking is the Trafficking in Persons (TIP) Report, which has been published annually by the United States State Department's Office to Monitor and Combat Trafficking in Persons since 2000.[19] Although compiled by the United States, the report attempts to provide an impartial assessment by country, breaking down whether victims are migrants from other countries or exported out of that country; which industries slavery is prevalent in; how victims are recruited and who is involved; and how the government has endeavored to work against these issues.

In the TIP Report, countries are ranked on a three-tier system, with Tier 1 indicating full compliance with the minimum standards outlined in the Trafficking Victims Protection Act (TVPA), and Tier 3 meaning that the country does not fully comply with the TVPA standards and its government is not making significant efforts to do so. These reports are a helpful place to start for a better idea of what human

---

18 "2018 Findings: Executive Summary." *Global Slavery Index*, 2018. The Walk Free Foundation (September 28, 2019).

19 "Trafficking in Persons Report." *State.gov*, June 24, 2019. U.S. Department of State (September 28, 2019).

trafficking looks like from country to country and how it has changed over time within each country.

WHAT'S YOUR FOOTPRINT?

What sustains this horrific crime? It can't be boiled down to a single factor—there are so many, all intersecting with each other: The vulnerability of individuals due to economic or emotional desperation. Weak justice systems that permit traffickers to conduct their business without fear of punitive consequences. The failure to identify victims because we aren't looking for them or the mislabeling of victims as criminals without realizing that there's more to their story. The difficulty of proving human trafficking cases in court, which then get prosecuted as a related, but different, crime. A failure to prioritize the issue in law enforcement and in business practices. The increasing complexity of globalization, which muddles supply chain transparency. The disconnected, at times contradictory, efforts of conscientious stakeholders including mobilization and advocacy NGOs (MANGOs), victim service providers, faith-based organizations, law enforcement, other government agencies, and prosecutors... the list continues.

And all of us are implicit contributors to the systems that allow modern-day slavery to persist. In our demand for cheap products and services, together with our lack of attention to hold our peers and our companies accountable for their behavior, we're passively encouraging a world that runs on slave services. In our willingness to turn a blind eye to the injustice happening all around us, we give traffickers free rein to operate unchecked.

It appears in the products you purchase: the devices you use, the food you consume, the clothes you wear... Oftentimes, even if we aren't consciously dehumanizing the individuals at the other end of the supply chain, we're so focused on snagging the most convenient deal that we hardly give a second thought to the story behind the prices. Was this cocoa harvested using child labor? Was this T-shirt made in a sweatshop? Or maybe, is this employee—at a restaurant or a massage parlor or even your neighbor's nanny—receiving the wages they should rightfully earn? Are they being treated with dignity? Could they quit this job if they wanted to?

You might be surprised by how much your lifestyle is intrinsically entangled in an injustice that often seems so distant. In 2011, the U.S. State Department partnered with the organization Made in a Free World to design an online survey called Slavery Footprint, where you can input your spending and lifestyle habits to get an estimate of how many slaves are "working" for you.[20] If you haven't yet seen the survey, you can find it at slaveryfootprint.org. I encourage you to go take it! It's an uncomfortable, but necessary, wake-up call. Even when I responded to each prompt as conservatively as possible, I was sickened by the realization that while pursuing

---

20 "How many slaves work for you?." *Slavery Footprint*, 2011. Made in a Free World (September 28, 2019).

my own quality of life, I unintentionally fueled the demand for forced labor.

In trying to save money by purchasing cheaper clothes, I didn't think about why those items might be produced and sold for less. In getting a new smartphone, I didn't realize that my demand for electronic devices was fueling horrific labor conditions for workers overseas. I bought dark chocolate and deliberated over vegetables and splurged on seafood without a passing thought to the people behind the products. My happiness meant misery for dozens of others.

But we have the power to change that.

We have the *responsibility* to change this. It's on us.

In September 2015, the United Nations adopted a series of Sustainable Development Goals, which included a commitment to end human trafficking by 2030. Specifically, Goal 8.7 resolves to "take immediate and effective measures to eradicate forced labour, end modern slavery and human trafficking and secure the prohibition and elimination of the worst forms of child labour, including recruitment and use of child soldiers."[21]

Can we make this happen?

So far, too many initiatives to combat human trafficking have focused on chasing the tails of traffickers who are always one step ahead; on well-intentioned but poorly

---

21 "#Envision2030 Goal 8: Decent Work and Economic Growth." *United Nations Department of Economic and Social Affairs*, 2016. United Nations (September 28, 2019).

enforced standards of ethical business practices; or on dramatic "kick-down-the-door" rescue operations without providing adequate support for survivors afterward, which makes them prone to being re-trafficked right back into the life they were briefly removed from. We can do better. As consumers, employees, investors, voters, and community members, we can each play a part in raising awareness of human trafficking and holding our world accountable.

Unfortunately, we've seen that technology has led to sinister changes in the landscape of exploitation. Traffickers now take advantage of Facebook, WhatsApp, and other social media platforms to pose as employment agencies or attentive boyfriends who offer irresistible opportunities.[22] Once they've lured victims into their control, they oversee or deprive their mobile phone use, disconnecting them from any way to reach out for help. In many ways, it's easier to deflect attention by conducting their business online, especially for sex traffickers. With the Internet and the dark web, they've been able to scale their activity while remaining more or less invisible.

However, that same technology can be leveraged to combat human trafficking from multiple angles:

---

22 Richmond, John. "Taking a Lesson From Traffickers: Harnessing Technology To Further the Anti-Trafficking Movement's Principal Goals." *U.S. Mission to the OSCE*, April 8, 2019. U.S. Mission to the OSCE (September 28, 2019).

- Measuring the problem in order to hone anti-slavery efforts where they are most needed.
- Preventing entrapment by providing greater supply chain transparency and more reliable labor recruitment.
- Identifying victims and enhancing communication between stakeholders for effective intervention.
- Disrupting buyers of sex trafficking as well as enabling consumers to choose products free of forced labor.
- Empowering survivors to reintegrate into society without the risk of being re-trafficked.

In the following chapters, we'll explore each of these ideas and much more. Are you ready?

CHAPTER 2:

CALLING ALL TECHNOLOGISTS

———

"Technology can and should be our vanguard in combating trafficking."

—PRINCESS EUGENIE OF YORK, CO-FOUNDER

OF THE ANTI-SLAVERY COLLECTIVE[23]

When I enrolled in that honors course on human trafficking as a first-year college student, I didn't know any technologists who were involved in the anti-slavery movement. It seems to me that human trafficking is simply not

---

23   Guilbert, Kieran. "UK royal, US ambassador tout tech tools to tackle human trafficking." *Reuters News Trust*, April 8, 2019. Thomson Reuters Foundation (September 28, 2019).

an issue that many tech-minded individuals think about—as a computer science student, I was surrounded by initiatives to increase diversity in the tech field; to teach programming in underprivileged schools; to bring technology to rural communities; to design accessible solutions for populations with disabilities; to develop systems to improve healthcare or preserve the environment or facilitate crisis response after natural disasters. All of these are such important missions, and I admire each one. However, I never heard about a project that tackled human trafficking of any kind.

But I believe the tide is changing. More and more, we're seeing technologists—from software engineers to IT specialists, from data analysts to user experience designers—coming alongside current anti-trafficking actors like government agencies and non-profit organizations. As they channel their cutting-edge expertise toward this cause, they'll carry the antislavery movement to a place of powerful impact, poised to disrupt and prevent trafficking until it is eradicated.

Now, I'd love to invite you into my own journey and introduce some of the people I've met along the way. These are individuals who were each stirred by injustice and found some way that they could wield their technical skills in the fight against slavery.

FROM PASSIVITY TO PURPOSE

Spring in Seattle always unfolds lackadaisically, which is how I felt on a particular Monday in April 2018. I'd already spent two quarters at the University of Washington but was still wondering, *What am I doing in computer science?* I didn't necessarily regret choosing this major—it's a highly coveted career path, after all, so I knew I should be grateful for it. However, while my peers chatted fervently about their interests in natural language processing, cybersecurity, and machine learning, I completed one coding assignment after another despairing that I would end up in a cubicle, in front of a screen, developing something that I didn't care about.

It was almost 1:30 p.m. when I found a seat for the first session of my honors class, called "Understanding and Combating Human Trafficking." I'd registered for it a few weeks back, at the time simply interested in learning more about the issue and finding answers to the questions I'd always been too uncomfortable to ask. No one had ever explained human trafficking to me, so I only had a vague, pieced-together understanding of the issue, and a connection to computer science had never even remotely crossed my mind.

All that was about to change.

The course was led by Dr. Kirsten Foot, a professor of communications at the University of Washington who researches cross-sector collaboration among different sectors working against human trafficking. At first, I must say I was intimidated by her wealth of expertise: she navigated such a nuanced issue with grace, candor, and sensitivity while I struggled to simply jot down my jumbled thoughts. As an opening activity, Dr. Foot asked my classmates and me to write down what we were hoping to get out of the course. I stared at my notebook, completely clueless. Lacking prior exposure to human trafficking, I had no idea what I *didn't* know, let alone what I wanted to learn.

The next ten weeks were a whirlwind! Underneath Dr. Foot's rigorous yet sympathetic guidance, I plunged into the devastating complexities of modern-day slavery that, quite honestly, redefined the way I understood the world. My heart ached for families in India who had spent generations in debt bondage and could not even envision a life of freedom; my stomach churned for the Albanian girls whose "boyfriends" persuaded them to leave their homes, then drugged and sold them for sex throughout Europe; my mind could not block out the men, women, and children in my own state, victims of labor or sex trafficking who pass through our hospitals and hotels and airports, yet nobody *sees* them.

The more I learned, the more I wanted to *do* something about it. In the spirit of the university's interdisciplinary honors program, our class examined the issue from a variety of angles according to stakeholder. What is law enforcement's role in eradicating human trafficking? How have various government agencies and policymakers been working? What are non-governmental organizations doing to provide services to survivors, raise awareness, or advocate for change? What about you and me, as consumers, employees, or investors? How can we make individual choices that contribute to the fight?

Could I find a way to get involved as a computer scientist? Surprisingly, the question didn't hit me until the end of the quarter, while I brainstormed topics for my term paper. Yet, even after I began searching for a relevance to my major, I struggled to identify the intersection of technology and anti-trafficking work. There was plenty of information about how traffickers exploited technology to entrap their victims and some mention of software that had been developed to disrupt that process, but I wanted to know what *I* could do.

It would take months before I'd realize the sheer depth of potential for leveraging technology against human trafficking, let alone figure out how I wanted to join the current efforts. However, a little spark of excitement came alive when I stumbled upon a project that a team of software developers had created during a recent hackathon, using blockchain technology to safeguard the recruitment process for Overseas Foreign Workers—individuals who find employment in a country where they do not have citizenship—so that no one could change the terms of their contract after they'd signed it. Project Handshake was being piloted in the Philippines in cooperation with ethical recruitment agencies.[24]

That was the moment when I realized I wasn't the only one. Somewhere out there, people were pushing the boundaries of

---

24 Andrews, Jordan. "Reducing Exploitation of Migrant Workers via the Blockchain—Handshake.tech." *Hackernoon*, September 24, 2017. Hackernoon (September 28, 2019).

technology to tackle different aspects of human trafficking with creative solutions. The possibilities were wide open!

That afternoon, I closed my laptop, went to the gym, and ran farther than I'd ever gone before—mile after mile, I felt like I was bouncing on a cloud. Crazy? Yes, but a turning point, nonetheless. From that moment, I began to enjoy my computer science classes because I knew I could potentially use those skills to make a difference for those still in slavery. Finally, I'd found motivation, which was crystallizing my future maybe not into a clearly defined plan but at least into a *purpose.*

CLOSING THE CHASM

Over the years, traffickers have consistently incorporated technological advancements to expand their exploitation of victims. In April 2019, United States Ambassador John Cotton Richmond raised this point during his keynote speech at the 19th Alliance against Trafficking in Persons Conference, hosted by the Organization for Security and Co-operation in Europe (OSCE) in Vienna, Austria. This two-day conference brought together representatives from governments, major international organizations, NGOs, business professionals, and academics who all shared a concern for incorporating technology into their respective spheres of influence to combat modern-day slavery.

Richmond described, "I have seen traffickers use technology to recruit victims – trolling through Facebook trying to start conversations with potential victims. One trafficker told me that, for every 150 contact attempts, one person would respond. They would start a conversation and one respondent out of ten would bite on his baited hook of deception."[25]

Recruiting victims via Facebook is just one example; when it comes to technology, traffickers have used it all. "Whether it is peer-to-peer file sharing, live streaming, encrypted chat rooms, multi-player online video games, social media, or new means of value transfer, if innovators come up with it, traffickers will use it as another tool in their exploitation toolbox," Richmond explained.[26] They manipulate technology to ensnare victims, to monitor their movement and control their contact with other people, to scale their profits and advertise their services—all while remaining relatively anonymous. "In a nutshell," Richmond continued, "we see traffickers using technology to help them do what they do more cheaply, more profitably, and more surreptitiously."[27]

In fact, "the misuse of technology has facilitated a scale of exploitation that seemed impossible only a decade ago," according to Valiant Richey, the OSCE Acting Coordinator for Combating Trafficking in Human Beings.[28] Together

---

25 Richmond, John. "Taking a Lesson From Traffickers: Harnessing Technology To Further he Anti-Trafficking Movement's Principal Goals." *U.S. Mission to the OSCE*, April 8, 2019. U.S. Mission to the OSCE (September 28, 2019).

26 Ibid.

27 Ibid.

28 "Using technology to combat trafficking in human beings: OSCE Alliance against Trafficking conference explores how to turn

with John Richmond and Britain's Princess Eugenie of York, Richey opened the OSCE conference in Vienna in front of more than 400 individuals from fifty-seven participating countries. Having formerly worked to incorporate artificial intelligence and online search platforms into criminal justice strategies in the Seattle area, Richey can attest to the indispensability of countering technology-facilitated trafficking with its own weapon. "The time has come for a change," he said. "We must harness technology as an asset in prevention, protecting victims and prosecuting traffickers."[29]

With that call to action, Richey alluded to the United States' distillation of anti-trafficking action into the "3P" paradigm: Prosecution of traffickers, Protection of victims, and Prevention of exploitation by disrupting the systems that make it possible.[30] Technology can bolster each of these three pillars in many ways. From social media platforms to specialized cybersecurity tools, technology already appears everywhere we turn—why should it be any different in the anti-trafficking space?

At first glance, however, there seems to be a disconnect between the often insular tech world and the anti-trafficking community, which includes people like police, prosecutors,

---

a liability into an asset." *OSCE Newsroom*, April 9, 2019. Organization for Security and Co-operation in Europe (September 28, 2019).

29 Ibid.

30 "3Ps: Prosecution, Protection, and Prevention." *Office to Monitor and Combat Trafficking in Persons*, 2019. U.S. Department of State (September 28, 2019).

victim service providers, or healthcare professionals. Unlike private businesses who seize the latest tech developments to maximize their profits, government agencies and non-profit organizations often lag appallingly far behind the cutting edge. If only they had the appropriate technologies, their efforts could be dramatically scaled for greater impact.

Why should technologists care about human trafficking? Precisely because we need to close the chasm between these two spheres. Incredible power is waiting to be unleashed; we just have to tap into it. It's high time that those of us in the anti-trafficking movement leverage the possibilities of the digital age to help us do *our* work cheaply and more effectively.

But that's not all.

Even more important than the technology are the technologists themselves. We don't need impersonal software solutions so much as we need a community united around this cause—individuals from every sector working together to influence change. It's a cause that can't be combated half-heartedly.

Let's hear from three of these individuals who have dedicated not just their work, but their lives, to the anti-trafficking mission.

IT STARTS FROM THE HEART

As I started to explore ways to contribute to the anti-trafficking cause through computer science, I thought of the organization that I'd volunteered for as part of my honors course: Seattle Against Slavery (SAS). In the fall of 2018, they revamped their website to include tech volunteering positions, including software engineering, data science, and user interface design. Of course, that sent me into flurries of excitement!

I'd already done some volunteering with fellow honors students to increase support for SAS—we'd asked passing students what came to mind when they heard the term "human trafficking," corrected their misconceptions, and let them know about organizations like Seattle Against Slavery, coalitions such as the Washington Anti-Trafficking Response Network (WARN), and Seattle-based Fair Trade organizations, including Theo Chocolate. However, I hadn't known that SAS was also involved in developing new anti-trafficking technology until I came across their updated website. I decided to attend their fundraiser at the end of October to learn more.

That's where I met Liz Rush, Anti-trafficking Technology Director for Seattle Against Slavery. After the formal presentations, I approached her while she was in the middle of recounting how she'd scrambled to salvage her slides after her cat had knocked wine onto her laptop. You'd never know it though—just minutes before, she'd taken the floor with her unceremoniously pithy style and roused a roomful of applause as she described feature after feature of SAS's ground-breaking new tech platform. Known as Freedom Signal, it's brilliantly slashing barriers to reach both buyers and victims trapped in the clutches of sex trafficking, in the Seattle area and beyond (See Chapters 5 and 6). And it's giving law enforcement officials, victim service providers, and government representatives a promising glimpse into the power of technology when it's fully integrated into existing anti-trafficking efforts.

In the frenzy of fundraiser mingling, there wasn't much time to chat. I told Liz that I was interested in getting involved as a tech volunteer—and I was surprised by her enthusiastic response. Scribbling her email address on a brochure, she generously offered to help me find a way to contribute to SAS's tech work, even though I was still an undergraduate student with, admittedly, little experience.

Still trying to figure out my own career path, I was curious: How had Liz done it? Serving as the anti-trafficking tech director for a local grassroots non-profit is quite the unique position. I was fascinated by the technical aspects of Freedom Signal itself but just as intrigued to find out how Liz found her way into this niche role, especially with so many other mainstream tech careers she could have chosen.

We met via video call a while later, and she was more than willing to share her story. "I have a longstanding interest in these kinds of issues," she began. Long before she entered the tech industry, she'd started volunteering at a domestic violence shelter when she was fifteen, deeply drawn to contribute whatever she could to promote freedom and safety in her community.

Even after she jumped into the tech world "on a whim" to explore the Seattle startup scene, Liz's enthusiasm lingered elsewhere. She drifted from startup to startup, feeling all the while a lack of personal fulfillment in creating technologies that she considered insular and unnecessary—for instance, yet another dating app. "When you're really involved in the tech world, it can be all about tech…" she lamented. It was aggravating to see so much misdirected effort, addressing needs that didn't really exist or that she wasn't personally passionate about.

The disconnect grew until she couldn't continue any longer. "I actually ended up stepping back from being really involved in the Seattle tech startup scene into just running my own consulting company for a couple of years," she remembers, "which allowed me to dedicate more time to volunteering." Yes, she knew that she could easily secure a comfortable, remunerative job in a well-established tech company, but she was more interested in pursuing the path of technology for social good. So with no regrets, she embraced the messy and unpredictable. For a few years, she volunteered for a victim support team connected with the Seattle Police Department that responded to domestic violence incidents. It didn't use her technology background at all. But "that's what really ignited my passion," she said.

During that time, she wrestled to reconcile the tension between her head and heart. Her "two different passions," technology and women's advocacy work, seemed hopelessly at odds.

Little did she know that in just a few months, she'd have the opportunity of a lifetime to pursue both at once.

Thanks to her volunteer manager who'd told her about other organizations to look into, Liz had been following Seattle Against Slavery on Facebook for a few months. She appreciated SAS's efforts to educate and mobilize the local community as well as advocate for policy changes to address human trafficking. One day, an open door unexpectedly fell into her lap when SAS posted that they were looking to hire a tech director.

Merging anti-trafficking and tech into a single career? It seemed too good to be true. So good, in fact, that for a while Liz didn't think she was qualified enough for such a niche position. "I tried to convince every single one of my friends to apply for the job because I thought they would be amazing at it," she remembers with a rueful smile.

Meanwhile, her friends kept telling her that *she* was the one meant for the job.

I asked her what finally persuaded her to take the position, and she shrugged. "It did take a long time," she admitted. But it helped once she "shifted [her] focus outside of the tech world." After meeting people from all professions working toward a common cause, she made the conscious choice to pursue the less trodden road of tech for non-profit. Since then, she hasn't regretted it.

In developing the Freedom Signal platform, Liz has been able to work on what she says is "by far, the most satisfying code I've ever written." Not only does she get to explore exciting applications of technology like sending automated text messages to phone numbers of potential victims scraped off of websites or designing social media ads to reach men who might be looking online to make a date to buy sex, she has the satisfaction of knowing that what she's doing is making a real difference in the world. "In 2018 alone, we helped over 1100 women connect to survivor advocates to get resources to exit prostitution, many of whom were victims of sex trafficking," she posted on LinkedIn, encouraging other software engineers to join her. "It feels *so* good to feel good about your tech job."

She's definitely inspiring others, including myself, to contribute their technical skills toward the anti-trafficking mission.

YOU CAN'T LOOK AWAY

In recent years, many technologists like Liz Rush have joined the fight against human trafficking. They've contributed by volunteering in their free time, getting together at hackathons to brainstorm innovative solutions, or developing apps or an analytical software platform that can be used by specific stakeholders. Everyone has a slightly different story of what pulled them into this space. Some became aware of the issue simply through reading news articles; others, like

Liz Rush, from the time they'd spent volunteering outside of the tech community. No matter what fueled it, the important thing was this: once they glimpsed the extent of the injustice that stripped people of their dignity and freedom, they couldn't look away.

For intelligence analyst Justin Underwood, it wasn't so much a choice as it was a compulsion. I connected with Justin while looking into Global Emancipation Network, a non-governmental organization leveraging big data analytics to disrupt human trafficking. He was glad to chat. "Not a lot of people talk about human trafficking, it's a subject that's hard to bring up with people," he told me. "It's really difficult to get a good understanding of it, and so I'm always willing to help people like yourself [who are] wanting to dig into it."

He spent some time describing his own experiences that kindled his passion for anti-trafficking work. "I'm more of an intelligence professional that works in the technology space," he explained. Currently he's working at Microsoft, but from 2006 to 2012, he served in the U.S. Army as a Human Intelligence Collector, where he conducted interrogations and managed source operations. "Korea was where I first encountered human trafficking," he remembered, learning that prostitutes were being smuggled from China and Russia into Busan, South Korea. "That was really my first exposure to it."

It was such a prevalent problem in Korea that he and his peers were briefed on the issue when they first arrived. "We discussed a lot of the human trafficking…I mean it was gross and abhorrent to see," he told me. "[Women] were brought over, being imported like a resource or material." Justin didn't directly participate in any trafficking-related investigations then, but that exposure heightened his awareness of the problem.

"Then I really got to see it firsthand when I was in Iraq," he continued, where he worked when ISIL was targeting a vulnerable population of Arab Christians, called Yazidis, to fund their activities through human trafficking. "I got to see more of it than I'd like to admit." He was absolutely disgusted by everything he saw. "So that was when I got hands-on experience," he said, "and that's really what inspired me to keep doing it."

What bothers Justin is not only the traffickers themselves but also the people who aren't doing anything to stop them. "It's the people that are complacent in it—that really frustrated me," he explained. "People don't care about problems until they're *their* problems." But for him, there are so many layers of injustice that he simply can't ignore the obligation to address it.

"Most of my experience has been with sex trafficking, and most of my recent experience has been with child sexual exploitation," he said, but he's familiar with the multitude of shapes and forms that human trafficking takes, including forced labor in the global supply chain. "Your cell phones are made by slaves, or at least the materials that are harvested to make the cell phones," he described as an example. "I have an Android sitting right beside me—it's really hard to detach yourself from somehow contributing, even inadvertently, to the human trafficking problem." From corporate business offices all the way down to the sources of raw minerals and crops, exploitation can be found at every step. Human trafficking is "the problem that everybody contributes to, but nobody realizes."

In the past years, Justin has volunteered for groups like Freedom Shield (formerly called Orphan Secure), a nonprofit comprised of law enforcement, intelligence, and military personnel who uncover networks of transnational criminal groups involved in child sex trafficking. Although he couldn't disclose too many details about his role with Orphan Secure, he said that he provided "subject matter expertise with regards to intelligence collection." On a general level, his focus is intelligence, which he defines as *actionable information*. "Intelligence has two purposes," he told me: "to inform decision-making and to drive operations." That's why this kind of data collection and analysis is so indispensable to anti-trafficking work.

More recently, he connected with Sergio Caltagirone, whom he had known through his work with Freedom Shield and Microsoft. When Sergio and his wife Sherrie started an organization called Global Emancipation Network (GEN), Justin contributed during GEN's initial stages of data analytics to provide strategic intelligence to those taking action against trafficking, including law enforcement officers, lawyers, and policymakers. Today, he's still involved with GEN where his expertise is needed.

Why does he do it? Because he can't *not* do something. "I'm just trying to find my lane, find my specialty, and see how I can contribute [and] push as hard as I can," he told me. What drives him is knowing that his work could mean the difference between dehumanization or dignity, and in some cases, between life and death.

GIVE IT YOUR ALL

Although the day-to-day demands of life often limit the time that tech volunteers can dedicate to anti-trafficking work, I talked with one man who has quite a different story. It's inspiring to meet people like Phil Bennett—those with a rare combination of vision and action—who devote themselves completely to the fight against modern slavery. He graciously agreed to call me from all the way in the UK to share his experiences at the intersection of technology and anti-trafficking work.

It started with low-commitment volunteering, circa 2014. After working at Hewlett-Packard for nearly fifteen years, Phil became a program architect at Salesforce, a software company enabling businesses to strengthen their customer relationships through cloud platform solutions. "It doesn't seem that long ago when I was [seated] in an airport after a difficult day," he remembers, "dejectedly staring at my laptop and searching for something more meaningful to me."[31] The good thing was that volunteering is "hardwired into the Salesforce culture."[32] Salesforce strongly encourages its employees to give back to the community: they're allowed to spend seven workdays each year volunteering with non-profit organizations.

In 2015, his journey took him to Kolkata, India, where he volunteered with Effect.org, a nonprofit organization providing vulnerable children with education, on an expedition to tackle sex trafficking. During his time there, he got an unforgettable glimpse of how children were being exploited in the city. He heard stories from survivors, learning about trauma that he could not fully comprehend. He also witnessed the challenges of providing survivors with education and employment to empower them to avoid exploitation in the future. Without some sort of support system, it's more than likely that these young survivors will be pulled right back into slavery. Their plight kept tugging at Phil. "I struggle[d] to process what [I'd] seen and to reconcile the scale of this tragedy with a world that seems to be oblivious," he remembers. "Frankly, it's difficult not to be affected."[33]

---

31 Bennett, Phil. "A new chapter in my career - let's tackle modern slavery." *Pulse*, October 18, 2018. LinkedIn (September 8, 2019).

32 Bennett, Phil. "Inspired by the Cause: Using Technology to Fight Human Trafficking—a Pro bono Story." *Salesforce Blog*, January 19, 2017. Salesforce (September 28, 2019).

33 Ibid.

That week-long trip changed Phil's life. "I decided that I would devote my free time to helping nonprofits in this field," he wrote in a blog post for Salesforce.[34] Around this time, he began to work with Unseen, the organization that operates UK's National Modern Slavery Helpline, to incorporate Salesforce's software systems into their operations. With Unseen's case management and referral services transferred onto a service cloud platform, helpline operators, government authorities, and social workers could better coordinate their efforts as they responded to crises that came in through the helpline. Instead of wasting time communicating basic information, they could address the important matters right away: providing care for survivors, apprehending perpetrators, and intervening to prevent dangerous situations. The platform also provided insights into the data that would enable Unseen to "paint a picture of the UK's slavery and trafficking activity," which would inform future policies and strategies.[35]

Phil took a year off from Salesforce in order to have the time to explore anti-slavery work. "Since that first expedition, my intense fury at the injustice and sheer barbarity of what I've seen has not diminished," he wrote on LinkedIn (Bennett 2018). During those months, he continued working with Effect.org as well as with a nonprofit called Destiny Foundation, a social enterprise in Kolkata where survivors

---

34 Ibid.
35 Ibid.

of sex trafficking can support themselves by creating fashion accessory products like bags and blankets. His empathy deepened as he interacted with the survivors at Destiny, fueling his desire to do whatever he could to support them in their unique journeys.

While he gained more on-the-ground experience with the realities of sex trafficking in India, Phil also spent a lot of time mulling over the issue on his own. He asked himself, "What are the big ideas that are being missed at the moment?" Although it didn't do any good to just sit and think about the problem, he realized it would be equally ineffective to throw himself into narrowly-focused work that missed the bigger picture. Already, he saw too many people with good intentions but little impact. "We need to be more ambitious with developing very high-scale solutions to modern slavery," he reflected, referencing the organizations collectively across the world that are tackling modern slavery.[36]

With his background in business and technology, Phil began to pay attention to areas that would benefit from unleashed resources. Particularly, he saw the need for boosting the capacity of nonprofit organizations by providing basic tech infrastructure, like laptops, data storage platforms, and communication networks—as well as the technical support they would need to maintain those systems. He also spotted the potential for implementing business strategies to enhance

---

36 Bennett, Phil. "A new chapter in my career - let's tackle modern slavery." *Pulse*, October 18, 2018. LinkedIn (September 8, 2019).

collaboration between these frontline organizations. If he could help nonprofits approach their work with the tactics used by for-profit firms, he was sure that they would be able to significantly increase their impact.

Always in the back of Phil's mind were the stories he'd heard from survivors who'd experienced horrors that no one should ever have to endure. Stories like that of Farzana (pseudonym), who'd eloped with a stranger she'd fallen in love with over the phone. He then brought her to a brothel where she was beaten, starved, and "trained" to serve between twenty and twenty-five men a day.[37] "When you take the time to really understand one person's story of being exploited, and then learn there are more than forty million other stories like that," Phil said, "how can it not jolt someone into action?"[38]

In October 2018, he announced his decision not to return to Salesforce, instead embracing "a mission to tackle modern slavery and human trafficking."[39] Currently, Phil is an advisor for Effect.org; he's a board member for Destiny Foundation; and he's a founding member of the initiative Tech Against Trafficking, a coalition of tech companies teaming up to innovate solutions for combating slavery. His goal is to bring the technical community closer to the problem to

---

37 Jha, Monica. "The Dark Hand of Tech that Stokes Sex Trafficking in India." *Factor Daily*, February 25, 2019. Sourcecode Media (August 20, 2019).

38 Bennett, Phil. "A new chapter in my career - let's tackle modern slavery." *Pulse*, October 18, 2018. LinkedIn (September 8, 2019).

39 Ibid.

synthesize new ideas and explore the high-scale possibilities of collaboration.

When I talked with him over the phone in February 2019, Phil was preparing to leave for the Code 8.7 Conference in New York. Organized in line with the UN's Target 8.7 to eradicate modern slavery by 2030, this conference was cohosted by Delta 8.7, the Alan Turing Institute, the Computing Community Consortium, the Tech Against Trafficking coalition, the University of Nottingham Rights Lab, and the Arizona State Global Security Initiative—the first-time ever gathering of these research communities around the antislavery mission. As one of the speakers, Phil was able to contribute his experience to the discussion: attendees participated in joint problem-solving sessions where they brainstormed ways to strengthen the utilization of computational science and artificial intelligence among anti-trafficking stakeholders.

Phil knows he's taken an unconventional path. "It's a strange irony that Salesforce's extraordinary culture of equality and 'giving back' has resulted in me leaving to pursue this passion," he wrote when announcing his career switch on LinkedIn (Bennett 2018). But he hasn't looked back. "I'm at the stage of my life where I'm willing to take a risk," he told me. "I'm more determined than ever to bring to bear all of the skills I've acquired in the private sector over the last 20 years to confront this problem."[40]

---

40 Ibid.

⁎⁎

We need more technologists like Liz, Justin, and Phil working on innovative ways to advance the antislavery movement. Like Liz, bridging the gap between the corporate and nonprofit worlds as the director of a tech volunteer team. Like Justin, who helps extract meaningful information from data so that it can be used on the frontlines. Or like Phil, who took a step back from the tech industry to strengthen interdisciplinary research and strategic collaboration. Listening to their stories, I've realized that no matter how big or small your role, no matter how many hours a week you devote, what's most important is that you think carefully about how you want to contribute and that you care deeply about the heart of the cause.

CHAPTER 3:

THROW TECH EGO
OUT THE WINDOW

"What are you willing to sacrifice in your life, what convenience are you willing to give up, in order to create the good that you want to see in the world?"

—ASHTON KUTCHER, CO-FOUNDER OF THORN[41]

At this point, it may be tempting to dive into developing some sort of technology to combat human trafficking right away. The potential is just sitting there, so why not get started?

---

41 "Ashton Kutcher on Using the Power of Technology for Good." *YouTube*, January 12, 2018. Salesforce Events & Dreamforce (September 28. 2019).

However, let's stop and check ourselves. The way we *approach* this kind of work as technologists is just as important as the work itself. In particular, we have to guard against an unconscious menace called "tech ego," an inflated confidence in the power of technology that distorts its realistic role within the anti-trafficking movement. If we're not careful, it will skew the way we develop and deploy technology in this space, ultimately damaging our ability to make a positive impact.

DUSTY, DISCARDED... AND SOMETIMES DANGEROUS

Unsuccessful technology is a topic that came up when I talked with Phil Bennett, the Salesforce program architect who left his career to work full-time against modern-day slavery. He shared some pain points that he's observed as a technologist in the anti-slavery space. For instance, "there's a whole graveyard of failed tech projects around, [developed] over the last few years—which is a shame." Then, as he unpacked how he's trying to identify the roots of these technology flops, Phil mentioned something that struck me deep between the ribs: "There's often a lot of ego wrapped around these technologies."

Tech ego.

For some reason, I couldn't get that phrase out of my mind.

For me, "tech ego" encapsulates technologists' perception that they can code up a solution, let it loose, and—*voila!*—it'll fix everything. It presupposes the beneficial power of technology without evaluating its true impact, let alone considering that technology might not even be needed at all. It operates within an isolated, often naive, view of the world.

"If you go to a tech developer and say, 'Hey, did it work?', they'll say, 'Oh, yeah, of course, it works.' We've got to penetrate beneath that," Phil told me. Because it's not just the technology itself—sure, we can develop perfectly functioning technology that does exactly what we programmed it to do. Our code can be written with the perfect syntax, execute the most elegant algorithms, and pass every one of our test suites, but we can't stop there. Even more than that, it's a matter of *how* that technology is used and whether it's actually having the positive impact that was intended.

Do we actually understand the problem that needs to be solved? And how do we ensure that the technology will appropriately address that problem?

Here's an example of a tech project that ended up in the "graveyard." A while back, United States Ambassador John Cotton Richmond, head of the U.S. Department of State's Office to Monitor and Combat Trafficking in Persons, visited another official who was in charge of enforcing his country's counter-trafficking policies. Richmond described their encounter at the 19th Alliance against Trafficking in Persons Conference held in Vienna, remembering that they'd "talked for hours about the challenges, successes, and failures that [the other official] had seen."[42]

During the course of their conversation, Richmond recalled that, thanks to a generous grant from a few years prior, some well-respected tech developers had designed a case management database for that country's counter-trafficking enforcement unit. "When I asked my new friend if I could see it and whether it was helping him do his job," Richmond said, "he laughed and dismissively shook his head. He then pointed to a dusty stack of boxes, paper, and computers in the corner of his office. The case management database was over there... and he told me that they never used it."[43]

What an unfortunate waste of grant money, brainpower, and time! Why didn't they use it? It wasn't because of ingratitude or a skepticism toward the technology. In this situation, it also wasn't due to a lack of capability on the part of the government official to learn how to use a complex database. He simply explained that "it was useless to him because it wasn't designed around what he needed."[44] Instead, "he turned his laptop around, showing me the screen, and told me that he tracks everything he can on a simple spreadsheet."[45] What

42 Richmond, John. "Taking a Lesson From Traffickers: Harnessing Technology To Further he Anti-Trafficking Movement's Principal Goals." *U.S. Mission to the OSCE*, April 8, 2019. U.S. Mission to the OSCE (September 28, 2019).

43 Ibid.

44 Ibid.

45 Ibid.

may have seemed like a spectacular solution from the developers' perspective ended up not being the most practical one after all.

This story is just one example of what can happen to the plethora of well-intentioned technological interventions in the anti-trafficking space. At best, these projects are ineffective and a waste of effort, like the dusty case management database Richmond described. At worst, they can make the situation more dangerous for those on the ground. For instance, Catharina Drejer, who co-authored #*Slavetech: A Snapshot of Slavery in a Digital Age* with anti-slavery expert Kevin Bales, is concerned that some anti-slavery apps are "simply dangerous."[46] Drejer gives the example of "a reporting app which, instead of reporting to the police or other assistants, aims to collect data for the [organization that created the app] itself."[47] Even if the data is secure, there's no way to know who's in control of it. "Such a collection is obviously problematic; this kind of information belongs to the police," Drejer explains. "This opens up the possibility of creating false apps run by traffickers who can thus collect large amounts of information, perhaps enough to disclose where a victim is."[48]

---

46 Drejer, Catharina. "«Tech for good» på sårbares bekostning [at the expense of the vulnerable]." *Skaperkraft*, January 25, 2019. Tankesmien Skaperkraft (September 28, 2019; translation).

47 Ibid.

48 Ibid.

It's tempting to latch onto technical projects—apps, database systems, machine learning algorithms, etc.—with the certainty that they'll be a game-changer in the anti-trafficking landscape. Sometimes, that makes it difficult to spot the conditions that complicate reality, preventing these technologies from being adopted in the way they were intended. We'll end up with brilliant technology that falls by the wayside, while the rest of the world isn't any better off for it.

What makes tech ego so slippery is that it's laced with good intentions. People want to use their skills and talents to help others who are suffering. But they also want to *see* their impact. They want to feel good about themselves and to be able to point to "the idea" that changed hundreds of people's lives for the better. They hope to leave a well-respected legacy behind them. Subtly, the focus shifts from playing a part to being the hero.

As I talked with technologists who have spent years developing software for anti-trafficking efforts, their experiences forced me to reevaluate my own reasons for wanting to be a tech volunteer for an anti-trafficking organization. Perhaps I was too eager to jump in and solve everything. Was it because I wanted to find a way to "save the day" as a computer scientist on the cutting edge? Was it only because I wanted to feel good about being in the tech industry or to have more experience to put on my resume?

The core of it boiled down to this:

Did my heart truly ache for the men, women, and children around the globe who have long forgotten what it's like to draw a breath of freedom? And was I willing to do whatever it took to enable them to seize that freedom for themselves?

NEED BEFORE SOLUTION

Although as far as I know, the term "tech ego" hasn't been specifically coined by anyone, it's a concept that's surfacing as people from different sectors begin to discuss the role of technology in ending slavery.

For instance, during the opening session of the OSCE 19th Alliance against Trafficking in Persons Conference in April 2019, U.S. Ambassador John Richmond delivered a keynote address in which he outlined several principles to consider when developing antislavery technology. Fundamentally, he emphasized *Need before Solution.* The last thing we should do, he said, is create "a solution in search of a problem."[49] When we approach it that way, we've got our priorities upside down.

Instead, Richmond explained that we should "begin with a clearly stated need and then search for a solution through the tech community."[50] This methodology will naturally open up a world of cross-sector collaboration because it "requires asking the people on the frontlines what their

---

49 Richmond, John. "Taking a Lesson From Traffickers: Harnessing Technology To Further he Anti-Trafficking Movement's Principal Goals." *U.S. Mission to the OSCE*, April 8, 2019. U.S. Mission to the OSCE (September 28, 2019).

50 Ibid.

specific needs are."[51] Truly seeking to understand what they're experiencing will puncture our sense of tech ego once we realize that our projects are only as valuable as their ability to address real needs.

If technologists dive into a project without first talking with law enforcement, service providers, survivors, etc. and asking them, "What do you need?" we'll end up spending money, time, and talent to develop something that will be useless, when we could have been investing those resources into something that would have actually helped. Remember the grant that funded the case management database in Richmond's story? Despite the intelligence, diligence, and noble intentions that fueled the project, it ended up a failure, discarded in a cobwebby corner.

Especially since the anti-trafficking space involves some of the world's most vulnerable individuals who often lack political agency, economic stability, and social support, Catharina Drejer urges that "we cannot afford to fail in the introduction of new technology in vulnerable groups."[52] Whether that solution involves technology or not, it should be centered around the trafficking victims and their legitimate needs, not our own—often misaligned—vision of success. "We must

---

51   Ibid.
52   Drejer, Catharina. "«Tech for good» på sårbares bekostning [at the expense of the vulnerable]." *Skaperkraft*, January 25, 2019. Tankesmien Skaperkraft (September 28, 2019; translation).

find the good solution *for* the vulnerable, and not at their expense," Drejer writes.[53]

We must look for a need before we brainstorm solutions, rather than the other way around. Nobody wins from trying to force a technological tool to have an impact where it's not necessary.

FIND WHERE IT FITS

Sometimes, the most immediate needs don't even involve technology—and that's okay.

On a snowy day in February, I talked with Robert Beiser, director of the NGO Seattle Against Slavery, who shared his own perspective of not squashing technology into a role unless it's really a valuable component. He majored in computer science in college and then worked for Microsoft for a number of years before launching full-time in the nonprofit sector, so I knew he had technical experience.

However, when I asked him how much his computer science background played into his work now, he laughed. "To be totally transparent, not that much. Essentially, we [at Seattle Against Slavery] have these...three areas of impact that we try to focus on: Education, Advocacy, and Prevention," he explained. The first one, Education, aims to help identify individuals in trafficking situations so that they can then be connected with the services they

---

53   Ibid.

need. This identification includes either victims recognizing their own condition or being noticed by other people in the community. However, trafficking cases are often unaddressed because people are misinformed about the mixture of force, fraud, and coercion that constitutes a legitimate slavery situation. That's why Seattle Against Slavery seeks to educate the community so that they are equipped with the knowledge to look out for something suspicious.

"The second piece, Advocacy," Robert continued, "was making sure that support was available [for trafficking survivors]." After a survivor has been identified, either by themselves or others, "they need a place to go, they need services to help them get on the way with the rest of their lives, and so a lot of the laws that we push for, and the policies that we push for, have been around support being available." As a grassroots organization, Seattle Against Slavery has been able to mobilize their local—and national—political community for real legislative change.

Education and Advocacy are great, but Robert added that "it's even better than either of those things if you can keep people from ever being hurt in the first place." That's where the third piece, Prevention, comes in... and out of it arose an opportunity where technology could make a difference. "We looked at the idea that the people who were exploiting folks in sex trafficking situations, in particular, were doing it online," Robert told me. Victims were "being posted on websites and then buyers and pimps and traffickers were exploiting them online."

What if SAS could somehow interrupt that process?

"We sort of traced through the idea that we could, while people were searching to buy trafficking victims online, get in the way and disrupt that a little bit," Robert said. "We could give them an education that would say 'Hey, you're hurting other people,' or 'Hey! This might be bad for your life.'" Beyond the legal implications of purchasing sex from a minor, they knew that many buyers also feel personal guilt and shame for their behavior; Seattle Against Slavery aimed to give these people the accountability they needed to break their habits. From there, SAS began to partner with software engineers to run search ads on browsers like Google or Bing, which would direct individuals to resources to learn about what's really happening when they buy sex online, as well as what they can do if they want to change their lifestyle.

That was around 2014. "It basically aligned with the same stuff we were doing in the real world," Robert said, "it was just that if you're going to be trying to tackle a problem that's occurring in a digital space, you're going to have to find digital solutions [for] dealing with that problem." While SAS still offers educational programs in high schools and support groups within the community, for example, they found that technology could fill a unique need for a targeted impact online—reaching people "who were pretty clearly searching to buy sex online and putting people at risk of trafficking," whom SAS might not otherwise be able to contact. It would be very hard to do that with physical methods, Robert explained, such as "putting up a billboard, or putting up a sign on the side of a bus."

But as far as his own technical skills go, Robert doesn't use them in his work today. "The type of computer science and coding work I was doing was not system integration work, so in my academic background the things that I learned how to do don't really connect at all to the work that we do," he explained. But he's fine with that, adding: "I think, being a person who was in the tech space for so long, I can understand a lot of the systems and processes in which the software gets written and tested and deployed, and that piece is really helpful."

Robert also recognizes the more subtle value of his experience at Microsoft, which informs his role now: "I function more as like a product manager, where my job is to get the pieces put in place that we know are going to be necessary for it to be successful [for potential partners]," he explained, "whether that's advocates who want to reach out to trafficking victims or law enforcement who want to find out what the prevalence of sex buying is in their area." His professional connections have been valuable as well, because "I know some of the people at Microsoft who have been helping on this project from my days back when I used to work there."

This is a great example of creating technology to address a problem that lent itself naturally to a digital solution and a technologist who leverages his skills where they're useful but always starts with the issue first and works backward from there to see what's truly needed.

IT DOESN'T STOP AFTER DEPLOYMENT

Even if we identify a real need that technology could address, there's more that we need to keep in mind to ensure that we'll actually deliver a successful product. For instance, it's necessary to understand the context in which the technology will be deployed: Will there be consistent Internet access? If you're creating an app for victims to use, do they have smartphones—will they be able to use an app? If you're designing software for a non-profit organization, will the social workers have the IT support they'll need when they (inevitably) need to troubleshoot? "No matter how impressive the system is," says John Cotton Richmond, or how well the app has been designed, these projects "will never have an impact" if the targeted user group doesn't have an accessible technological infrastructure in which to deploy that system.[54]

If it isn't accessible, it fails to be relevant.

We also need to be realistic about technology's role within preexisting operations, shooting for simple and usable technology rather than overly sophisticated systems that no one

---

54 Richmond, John. "Taking a Lesson From Traffickers: Harnessing Technology To Further he Anti-Trafficking Movement's Principal Goals." *U.S. Mission to the OSCE*, April 8, 2019. U.S. Mission to the OSCE (September 28, 2019).

will be able to manage. "Simplicity will help maximize adoption and implementation of each new technology," Richmond explains, harkening back to his interaction with the other counter-trafficking enforcement official by adding that "the fewer fields in a database, the more likely people on the ground will fill it out."[55]

In Phil Bennett's years of experience, he's become all too familiar with the implications of a lack of context that arises from the disconnect between software developers who want to make a difference and the frontline organizations who are actually involved in the identification, rescue, and reintegration of survivors. Specifically, he told me about the barrier of IT literacy, especially in the nonprofits that he's worked with in India. There's a lot of complicated technology being deployed to nonprofits, which seems exciting from our end—but when we actually look at how those nonprofits are conducting their day-to-day operations, the technology seems to have "disappeared."

What happened to those software systems? Either the staff didn't understand how to use it efficiently, they didn't have a close relationship with a technologist who could help maintain and operate it, or they weren't able to easily customize it to fit their needs. "It's not really a responsible way of developing technology," Phil said. Many people who work in nonprofit or other sectors related to trafficking know very

---

55 Ibid.

little about how to deploy technology, so it's almost pointless to give them complex software systems designed to revolutionize their work. If we aren't going to make sure they're equipped with the knowledge and support to make the most of the technology, we may as well be tossing that project directly into the "graveyard."

As the director of the Multi-stakeholders Initiative for Accountable Supply Chain of Thai Fisheries (MAST) Coalition based in Bangkok, Thailand, Dornnapha Sukkree corroborated Phil's observations with her own perspective. Although she'll be the first to admit that she's "only a user" who knows very little about technology, I called her from the other side of the ocean to hear about MAST's involvement in deploying location-tracking systems within local fishing communities. Far away from the oversight of government authorities, employees are at risk of brutal exploitation at sea, forced to work exhausting hours in degrading conditions, forbidden to leave. One way MAST works against this is by partnering with a company called Pelagic Data Systems to install tracking devices on fishing vessels. With this technology, they're able to monitor the vessels' movement for any illegal or suspicious patterns that might indicate forced labor on board—for instance, if workers are kept at sea for abnormally long stretches of time.

Dorna's unique role, overseeing the pilot program for these devices, has convinced her of the importance of integrating technological interventions seamlessly into the daily routines of the fishermen. "Technology is helpful," she told me, "but you have to work well with people who are already there." This is especially true for users like the local fishermen, and even Dorna herself, who have little prior technical training. "People who use it have to know the highest potential of the technology and how to use it," she said. "It's like if you have a smartphone but you don't know what it's made for." That's why members of the Pelagic Data Systems team frequently go out to talk with the fishermen, to hear their feedback and make sure that their technology is actually poised to have the impact they envision.

Otherwise, it would end up as simply a contraption screwed onto a boat, not being useful to anybody.

REAL WORLD VS. DIGITAL WORLD

Lastly, we must define from the very beginning how we'll measure the impact of the technology intervention on human trafficking. We can't just assume that it's doing what we designed it to do—we need to be constantly engaged with the community that's using the technology. "No one person, one group, or one intervention will win the day," Richmond said. "We must collaborate for a specific purpose."[56]

A large part of that involves the realization that our project goes beyond technology. It requires stepping out of the purely digital realm to see how it interacts with the real world.

---

56 Ibid.

"The anti-trafficking space is not a technology space," Robert Beiser told me. "Relationships with human beings is how a lot of people get out of trafficking situations, and the types of support that are necessary when people get out of trafficking situations is very one-to-one, it's relationship-based." Once we begin introducing technology into these interventions, it becomes "a different paradigm." We have to critically examine the ways that technology can either enhance or replace existing methods—as well as identify the cases where a technological solution is not called for at all.

A careful understanding of the real vs. digital intersection informs the way that Seattle Against Slavery develops their technology platform. For example, Robert said, "we've seen with technology that text-based support can be incredibly effective" when reaching out to local sex trafficking survivors. "Part of it is just understanding how technology can do things in a different way that might be *more* successful than the way that we're currently supporting trafficking victims." However, it's also important to realize when technology doesn't have a place: that's why SAS hasn't brought as much of a technological focus to combating forced labor.

When I asked Robert about it, he said that actually, "we've tried to work the labor trafficking space as well." But at the moment, "people aren't recruiting labor trafficking victims quite as much through technology, at least in the [United States]." Technology interventions have been successful in fighting sex trafficking because it's technology disrupting technology. But the labor trafficking environment in the United States isn't currently as conducive to technical solutions.

Robert's explanation helped me realize that recognizing the limits of technology is just as important as recognizing its potential. Technology is not always the answer to every problem—we shouldn't expect it to solve everything. "There is no fast forward button, no magic tech wand we can wave to make everything easier," Richmond cautioned. "While technology can advance our goals... there is not an algorithm or app that is going to stop trafficking" (Richmond 2019). Even so, when it's focused in the right ways, technology can be a powerful tool to "help people do their jobs more effectively, arrest more traffickers, and serve more survivors."[57] Within its realistic capabilities, we should leverage it to its fullest potential.

We need to direct our energies into the development of technologies that will help us move forward in the fight to eradicate modern-day slavery.

How do we know where to focus our efforts? How can we know which technical interventions will make a difference? In order to do this right, we technologists need to work closely with the stakeholders on the frontlines to understand what's truly needed and what will truly be useful. That takes a lot of humility!

---

57   Ibid.

I believe this sort of humility—letting go of the need to prove yourself and instead shifting your focus to "How can I serve?"—is the antidote to tech ego. And you have to get your hands dirty in order to cultivate it...

GET ON THE GROUND!

What's the best way to crush that tech ego? With everyone I talked to, time and again their answer echoed the same thing: We must see what's happening on the frontlines, learn from the people working across fields, and be exposed to the complexities and cultural challenges of tackling slavery in the real world. We need to *understand* the problem before we figure out our place in the fight.

In other words, get yourself on the ground!

As the technology director for Seattle Against Slavery, Liz Rush reflected, "What really did it for me was being involved in the community outside of the tech world. When I shifted my focus outside of the tech world, volunteering in different sectors, I met people in other types of industries: health-care, service, lawyers who were all volunteering with this [issue]." That cross-sector interaction continues in her job today. "I get to interact with people all the time who are not in the tech world," she said. They may not "know anything about JavaScript, but they're the experts about how to actually help people. It's been really humbling." Working with people with vastly different skill sets, yet with a common unifying goal, is one of the best ways to deflate the notion that you have all the answers because it situates you in a bigger perspective, a broader conversation, where you can put your abilities into context.

"I'm not the expert when it comes to the things that you need to do to help people who are being exploited," Liz continued. "My technical knowledge is only valuable in so much as it facilitates the work of other people who have more experience doing direct services [to victims]." That's why it's so important for her to understand how law enforcement and victim service providers operate—the more she interfaces with their daily challenges, the more she can hone her efforts as she comes alongside them.

Justin Underwood, an intelligence analyst at Microsoft who's seen human trafficking firsthand and has volunteered for various anti-trafficking organizations over the years, feels the same way. When I talked with him, he emphasized the hands-down importance of understanding what's actually happening on the ground and how your technology will be applied to those operations. "The most important advice is you need to understand how that intelligence is used," he told me, "whatever... technology you're creating."

He continued, "You need to understand how a person uses that information. I'm talking about law enforcement, I'm talking about military... the people who go and act upon the information that you give them." With years of experience in the U.S. military's "kick-down-the-door" interventions to rescue sex trafficking victims, Justin warned against the pitfalls of not understanding the context that you're developing technology for, especially when it comes to such high-stakes operations. He said, "I've worked with people before who've never had done any field experience, never done a kinetic operation—honestly, it's a different mindset once you've been there. It's extremely important."

In many cases, it's a necessary wake-up call for technologists. "It's so easy to get pigeonholed into your own research, your academic understanding of this problem... to just get caught up in your own sort of projects," Justin told me. Instead, "it is extremely important [to] understand how the technology or intelligence provided is being used." What does that look like? "I'm not saying you have to go kick down a door," Justin explained, "I'm saying just go *talk* with them." Maybe simply opening a conversation is, in its own way, kicking down the door to bridge the disconnect between technologists and those on the frontlines, paving the way for responsibly developed projects.

For Phil Bennett, volunteering with nonprofit organizations gave him a tangible sense of the current situation to which he could then bring his technical expertise. In fact, it's been so transformative that he wishes he'd done more volunteering when he was younger, rather than going straight into work. He said that during his time in India, "I realized quite quickly that in order to have any kind of understanding of the application of technology I needed a better understanding of the nature of human trafficking and the human cost of it." His experiences working with Effect.org and Destiny Foundation in Kolkata as well as with Unseen in the United Kingdom were pivotal to his understanding of the "personal stories behind the numbers," which lends purpose as he thinks about the human impact of his projects.[58]

"There are a lot of tech people who want to be involved—and you're one of them," he told me. But it takes a lot of effort for someone in the tech world to actually get expertise in what modern slavery's actually about, and the real-world hurdles associated with it. At the end of our conversation, Phil offered to help me find an internship with a nonprofit in India or elsewhere, to get firsthand experience on the frontlines of the anti-slavery movement. He also encouraged me to spend some time thinking deeply, exploring these issues, understanding the challenges of tackling modern-day slavery.

While I haven't taken him up on his internship offer yet, I *have* been following his advice to "have a think," examining my own motives that have drawn me into the anti-slavery space as well as clarifying the direction I want to pursue with my future. The more I discover, the further I am from having it all figured out. Of one thing I'm sure: there *is* a place for technology in this mission, but its role is far from isolated. It's only one facet of an intricate, international, interdisciplinary endeavor to wrest out a sickening injustice by the roots.

I hope that means my tech ego is shriveling.

---

58 Bennett, Phil. "A new chapter in my career - let's tackle modern slavery." *Pulse*, October 18, 2018. LinkedIn (September 8, 2019).

PART 2:

DEVELOPING THE TECHNOLOGY

"It's not about one of us doing it all, it's about all of us doing what we can."

—KELLY WELK

CHAPTER 4:

TRACK DOWN THE TRAFFICKERS

"It's...really promising that the very technologies traffickers are using to bring their [human] product to market...[are] the very same technologies that we can use against them to combat trafficking."

—SHERRIE CALTAGIRONE, EXECUTIVE DIRECTOR

OF GLOBAL EMANCIPATION NETWORK[59]

One of the reasons why human trafficking remains such a pervasive problem is because of the status quo that allows

---

59 Magee, Tamlin. "Inside GEN, the nonprofit combatting human trafficking with big data." *Computerworld*, January 11, 2019. IDG Communications (September 28, 2019).

traffickers to ensnare, exploit, and profit off their victims with scarcely any fear of being caught. In remote areas such as the deserts of India or the waters off the coast of Thailand, men, women, and children are forced to work in brutal conditions without the hope of anyone ever seeing them to intervene. And within the depths of the dark web, perpetrators hide behind duplicitous profiles while posting sex ads and abusive pornographic content.

For years, these traffickers have enjoyed unparalleled anonymity—but the data is *there*. "It's knowing the right places to look," says Sherrie Caltagirone, founder of a non-profit organization called Global Emancipation Network. "You really don't have to look very hard at all to find it."[60] Both digital and physical fingerprints leave traces of their whereabouts, and if we can tap into those clues, we could accelerate the process of rescuing victims and bringing criminals to justice. We could even glean insights to predict traffickers' future movements, which would boost us from playing "catch-up" to taking a more proactive position.

However, law enforcement simply doesn't have the bandwidth to sift through millions of images or ads in order to crack a case. Even if they did have infinite time and personnel, there are many patterns that humans would easily overlook, not to mention the psychological toll of being immersed in

---

60 Ibid.

that material for hours. Making sense of this data is like finding a needle in a haystack: tedious, painful, and pretty near impossible.

Thankfully, that's where technology comes in!

SPOTTING SLAVERY FROM SPACE

At the University of Nottingham in the United Kingdom, one team of researchers discovered that they could pull data from satellite images to identify sites of labor trafficking from space. Who would have thought that in order to pinpoint a crime on the ground, we'd have to zoom out to an astronaut's view?

As research director at the university's Rights Lab and a professor in the School of Politics and International Relations, Kevin Bales has been committed to the fight against contemporary slavery for years. He is the co-founder of Free the Slaves, an international organization that campaigns for liberation on a comprehensive cross-sector level, as well as the author of several books on the status of modern slavery. He was also involved in creating the Global Slavery Index, an annual country-by-country ranking of the prevalence of enslaved people, the relevant risk factors and trade flows, and government anti-slavery action (or lack thereof).

Bales' interest lay especially in South Asia's brick kiln industry, where up to sixty-eight percent of its estimated 4.4 to 5.2 million workers, nineteen percent of whom are under eighteen years old, are thought to be trapped in forced labor.[61] Many of these workers enter their jobs voluntarily, hoping for better wages or to pay off a loan. "Individual migrants and migrant families are told they can live and work, and that food will be provided and they will be given a bit of an advance," he explains. "But then, once on-site, they find there a couple of thugs who have complete physical control."[62] Men, sometimes pregnant women, and young children alike are forced to work in grueling conditions, sometimes for generations.

One woman called Puspal says that she'd started working to pay off a debt that soon proved to be bottomless: "My family had been working in a kiln [in India] for five years but didn't seem to be earning any money. Whenever we asked, the debt was still not paid."[63] The traffickers exploited their desperation in order to recruit even more slaves. "On a promise of a commission we brought more families from Chhattisgarh," Puspal remembers, "but the new workers were not paid and were starving. They tried to leave, but two got caught and they locked them up and beat them."[64] Digging clay, shaping and firing bricks, staggering under the weight

---

61 Mitra, Dakhina and Delphine Valette. "Brick by Brick: Environment, Human Labour & Animal Welfare." *The Brooke*, 2017. International Labour Organization, The Brooke Hospital for Animals, and The Donkey Sanctuary (September 28, 2019).

62 Beaumont, Peter. "Experts reach for the stars to fight slavery as satellite pictures tell all." *The Guardian*, March 19, 2018. Guardian News & Media Limited (September 28, 2019).

63 "India: debt bondage." *Anti-Slavery*, 2019. Anti-Slavery International (September 28, 2019).

64 Ibid.

of dozens of bricks at a time, some people spend their entire lives in this kind of bonded labor.

It's a system that operates with little to no government oversight, yet even if a government wanted to institute or enforce labor rights, locating the sites of slavery can be elusive. Then Bales discovered an unlikely repository of clues: satellite images.

He got his first glimpse at this hidden potential around 2016, investigating child labor in unregulated fish-drying camps in Bangladesh. Two such camps in Sundarbans National Park, in southwest Bangladesh, had already been suspected of forcing children as young as nine to work for up to forty hours straight. He had spoken to nine escapees from the camps, hearing stories about what it was like: Sleeping outside. Scarce food. Disease. Bengal tigers. Sexual abuse. All so that fish could be dried, packed, and processed into pet food.

While such makeshift camps are permitted in the park during certain months of the year, Professor Bales had learned from the escapees that several of the camps had remained there for two or three years. The local authorities denied awareness of any malpractices, but Bales had a hunch that there were more camps tucked in the reserve forest, getting away with appalling abuses. He was determined to find them.

Astonishingly, Bales noticed that images taken by satellites, such as the ones publicly available on Google Earth, contained distinguishable signs of labor trafficking. "What look like buildings on the satellite images are not in fact buildings, but giant racks where children who have been enslaved have been doing the drying and cleaning and scraping," he explained.[65]

Using image analysis techniques, Bales was able to locate five additional labor camps, findings that he presented to the Houses of Parliament in October 2016. "With the fishing camps," he said, "suddenly we were able to say to the authorities, 'Here are five more camps you say that you have no record of.'"[66] Traffickers who'd spent years exploiting these children in the national park now found themselves under scrutiny. And knowing *where* the slaves are, Bales knew, was the crucial first step toward freedom.

Bales knew he was on the brink of a vastly unexplored technology, and he wanted to leverage its potential to support policymakers and NGOs on the ground to help stop slavery "as it begins to happen, not wait until after it's happened."[67] From over 100 scientists, geographers, engineers, and computer specialists at the Rights Lab, he assembled

65 McGoogan, Cara and Muktadir Rashid. "Satellites reveal 'child slave camps' in Unesco-protected park in Bangladesh." *The Telegraph*, October 23, 2016. Telegraph Media Group (September 28, 2019).

66 Beaumont, Peter. "Experts reach for the stars to fight slavery as satellite pictures tell all." *The Guardian*, March 19, 2018. Guardian News & Media Limited (September 28, 2019).

67 McGoogan, Cara and Muktadir Rashid. "Satellites reveal 'child slave camps' in Unesco-protected park in Bangladesh." *The Telegraph*, October 23, 2016. Telegraph Media Group (September 28, 2019).

a team of researchers who caught onto his vision: individuals like Dr. Doreen Boyd, a specialist in the use of remote sensors on helicopters, satellites, and other aerial vehicles to collect measurements of Earth; and Dr. Jessica Wardlaw, a research associate from the School of Geography who'd just finished a project to create 3D models of the surface of Mars. Together, they would build "the world's first large-scale research agenda for ending slavery."[68]

Doreen Boyd, who now runs the data program at the Rights Lab, estimates that "one-third of all slavery is visible from space, whether in the scars of kilns or illegal mines or the outlines of transient fish-processing camps," which makes satellite images a prime resource for anti-trafficking work.[69] No one had really thought to look before, but once they noticed it, the signs were obvious. "The brick kilns in Pakistan I looked at, and sites like charcoal camps in Brazil, are so big—and had such unique patterns," Bales added. The team decided to start with brick kilns because the "distinctive, circular nature" of the dusty brown ovals made them easy to identify (Global News). They can be 150 meters long,

---

68 Ounsworth, Rob. "Professor Kevin Bales; how science can help end slavery." *University of Nottingham Blog*, February 3, 2017. University of Nottingham (September 28, 2019).

69 Scoles, Sarah. "Researchers spy signs of slavery from space." *Science Mag*, February 19, 2019. American Association for the Advancement of Science (September 28, 2019).

with chimneys that are distinctive even from space. "You cannot mix them up with something else," Boyd says.[70]

"At a very basic level," says Jess Wardlaw, "we can hope to improve our understanding of the activity, how it actually takes place... how these sites are moving over time. [We can] investigate whether there are any trends in where the brick kilns and other slavery activities are taking place."[71] With about 600 satellites in orbit to observe the earth, they had a "profusion of high-resolution, freely available satellite data" that would enable them to estimate the numbers of enslaved people as well as the sites where they're located.[72]

Too much data, in fact, for them to handle alone.

If they wanted to scale their project to analyze thousands of satellite images from Google Maps, they were going to need some help. Eventually, computers would be able to identify potential signs of slavery for them, but Jess Wardlaw explains that when it comes to extracting meaning from images, "computers remain inferior to even the most untrained human eye" (Seelochan 2017). "We have to 'teach' machines to identify the kilns for us," says Doreen Boyd.[73]

70 Scoles, Sarah. "Researchers spy signs of slavery from space." *Science Mag*, February 19, 2019. American Association for the Advancement of Science (September 28, 2019).

71 Vomiero, Jessica. "U.K. researchers use Google satellite images to identify signs of slavery in India." *Global News*, August 6, 2017. Corus Entertainment (September 28, 2019).

72 "Fighting slavery from space." *Vision*, no. 03 (2019). University of Nottingham (September 28, 2019).

73 Ibid.

The first step was personally labeling these pictures so that the computer would be able to infer patterns that indicated a brick kiln. The researchers would look at images one by one, clicking on specific areas where kilns were visible. These images would eventually make up a sizable set that they would then use to train the machine-learning model. However, manually going through to mark images for a training set was exhausting and inefficient. "My PhD student, Bethany Jackson, had to sit and look at every image to identify what she thought was a brick kiln," Dr. Boyd remembers.[74]

So they decided to turn to crowd-sourcing. May 2017 marked the launch of their "Slavery from Space" project through zooniverse.org, enabling anyone online to help identify brick kilns in satellite images of South Asia—specifically, a 2600-square-kilometer area in the desert state of Rajasthan, India, which is part of a region stretching across Pakistan, India, Bangladesh, and Nepal called the "Brick Belt," containing tens of thousands of brick kilns. Through the project, the researchers recruited about 100 online volunteers who were then shown a series of images. All the volunteers had to do was click on the areas of the image where they recognized a brick kiln.[75]

As the saying goes, many hands make light work. One volunteer, Julian, said that it's "an easy task that can be

---

74 Ibid.
75 "Slavery From Space." *Zooniverse*, 2017. University of Nottingham Rights Lab (September 28, 2019).

done by anyone with a computer and broadband, anywhere, and at any time convenient."[76] Added up, these simple tasks become extremely powerful. Thanks to the volunteers' participation, Kevin Bales and his team were able to gather an initial dataset of 396 hand-tagged images, containing over 6000 classified brick kiln sites, by the end of June. "THANK YOU so much to everyone who steamed through the annotation of our first batch of images, we're truly overwhelmed by your response!" they posted on their zooniverse webpage.

Then, they partnered with colleagues from the School of Computer Science to train artificial intelligence algorithms with the volunteer-tagged images to extrapolate relevant information in order to recognize kilns in images taken in other areas of the Brick Belt. "Once we've trained the algorithm, we can be pretty confident that it can look at other images and accurately spot a brick kiln," Boyd said. "We can amalgamate this feature identification with the crowd's results and we can be, say, 95% certain that there are brick kilns in a specific location."[77] In fact, in January 2019, the Rights Lab reported in the journal *Remote Sensing* that their

76 Wardlaw, Jessica. "Slavery from Space: Citizen Science in the Antislavery Movement." *SciStarter*, April 6, 2019. Arizona State University and the National Science Foundation (September 28, 2019).

77 "Fighting slavery from space." *Vision*, no. 03 (2019). University of Nottingham (September 28, 2019).

algorithms could correctly identify 169 of 178 kilns from Google Earth, which is almost exactly 95%.[78]

From there, they're able to pass the coordinates of potential slavery sites to local NGOs to investigate further. As they communicate with organizations on the ground about potential slavery sites, they're able to cross-reference the data to confirm whether certain sites are truly operated with slave labor. "You have to have verification on the ground that what you think you see is actually there," says Dr. Boyd. That would give the NGOs a clearer direction on the ground, enabling them to visit previously unknown locations to verify if people are enslaved there. And it will, in turn, improve the accuracy of the insights they glean from the machine-learning models.

So far, the efforts of Professor Bales and the Rights Lab team have been building momentum toward "[guiding] the rescue and rehabilitation of thousands of enslaved people."[79] As of February 2019, one of the kilns detected by their technology had been raided, "resulting in the freedom of twenty-four slaves."[80] As they expand their partnerships with law enforcement and other local organizations, and as their

---

78 Scoles, Sarah. "Researchers spy signs of slavery from space." *Science Mag*, February 19, 2019. American Association for the Advancement of Science (September 28, 2019).

79 Ounsworth, Rob. "Professor Kevin Bales; how science can help end slavery." *University of Nottingham Blog*, February 3, 2017. University of Nottingham (September 28, 2019).

80 Davis, Matt. "One-third of all slavery is visible from space." *Big Think*, February 22, 2019. Big Think Edge (September 28, 2019).

technology improves, hopefully those numbers will continue to increase.

This satellite image analysis technology is especially useful in countries where the governments are already willing and wanting to abolish forced and child labor within their borders but don't know where the locations are. For example, the 2019 Trafficking in Persons (TIP) report noted that the government of Bangladesh has made "significant efforts" to eliminate trafficking by adopting a national action plan, convicting traffickers, and investigating accusations of potential trafficking crimes but still needs to prioritize "proactively screen[ing] for trafficking indicators and identify[ing] victims in vulnerable populations and areas."[81] Like Bangladesh, the other countries that comprise the Brick Belt—India, Pakistan, and Nepal—were placed on the Tier 2 Watch List in the 2019 TIP report. The Rights Lab's new remote sensing technology can help them concentrate their anti-trafficking efforts.

The researchers at the Rights Lab are already brainstorming bigger and brighter ideas. Kevin Bales has been talking with satellite companies to access more detailed images in addition to the ones available for free on Google Maps. He also mentioned the possibility of intra-university collaboration, such as with the Nottingham Geospatial Institute, to

---

81 "2019 Trafficking in Persons Report." *State.gov*, June 2019. United States Department of State (September 28, 2019).

improve the data gathering and analysis from other regions of the world.[82]

As of 2019, they've released a second set of images for volunteers to sift through. At the beginning of April, Dr. Wardlaw announced that they'd released 100,000 images of India and Pakistan, planning the project timeline around Citizen Science Day, April 13th: "The race is on!" (Wardlaw 2019). For this second round, they partnered with Digital-Globe, a geospatial data company that has similarly recruited citizens to scrutinize satellite images for boats on Ghana's Lake Volta, where children are forced into fishing work. This is collaboration at its finest: a partnership between academics, tech professionals, and everyday people who want to make a difference.

Does labeling satellite images sound like a great volunteer opportunity for you? If you'd like to participate in this project, you can find more information about how to get involved here: www.zooniverse.org/projects/ezzjcw/ rights-lab-slavery-from-space

Bales' research lab also plans to expand the project to other industries where slave labor is unfortunately, not uncommon. This includes open-pit charcoal mines in the Democratic Republic of the Congo, cotton harvesting in Turkmenistan, or shrimp farms in South Asia. Although the

---

82 Ounsworth, Rob. "Professor Kevin Bales; how science can help end slavery." *University of Nottingham Blog*, February 3, 2017. University of Nottingham (September 28, 2019).

sites themselves can be tricky to spot from space—they're not as distinctive as the brick kilns—there are other clues that indicate the presence of a labor camp: workers at a shrimp farm will clear the area of mangrove trees, and children in cotton fields harvest the crops by hand. For these scenarios, the Rights Lab partners with a company called Planet, which provides lower-resolution images that are captured at a high frequency by 150 small satellites.[83] By analyzing how fast the cotton or trees are being cleared, the researchers can determine whether it's being done by machine or hand. These signs will give insight into whether slavery could be present at that site.

As Bales and his team are able to broaden the scope of their research, and as their machine-learning models become more accurate over time, we'll be able to bring more traffickers to justice and slaves to freedom… because they will no longer be invisible.

STRATEGIC WARFARE

If the rugged terrain of labor trafficking is challenging to navigate, the labyrinth of the dark web is just as daunting. Containing encrypted content that's invisible to conventional Internet browsers, the dark web offers its users the ability to access a vast online network with a significant degree of

---

83 Scoles, Sarah. "Researchers spy signs of slavery from space." *Science Mag*, February 19, 2019. American Association for the Advancement of Science (September 28, 2019).

anonymity. Unfortunately, this makes it conducive to illegal activity such as sex trafficking and child pornography.

Deciphering the transactions that occur on the dark web used to be nearly unthinkable. In order for investigators to pinpoint trafficking activity, they have to not only disentangle but also synthesize and analyze, massive amounts of information in order to track trafficking activity on the dark web—and they need to do this *fast* in order to respond to situations effectively.

One woman claimed this as her mission and set out to tackle it head-on.

Her weapon? Big data.

Sherrie Caltagirone has to be one of the most inspiring individuals I've met. Radiating razor-sharp vision and perseverance, she's a homeschooling mother of four who jokes that her superpower is the ability to do a lot on little sleep. As if that's not enough, she's also the tireless face behind Global Emancipation Network, a non-profit organization harnessing the power of big data to disrupt human trafficking.

At nineteen, Sherrie discovered her heart for anti-trafficking work through an internship with the Protection Project, a human rights research institute at Johns Hopkins University. She gained firsthand experience contributing to legislation for trafficking prevention, and it wasn't long before she was "hooked for life."[84] From there, Sherrie continued to

---

84 Thorpe, Devin. "The New Sheriff In Human Trafficking Is Wielding Big Data." *Forbes*, October 11, 2018. Forbes Media (September 28,

engage with government agencies, rescue organizations, and other NGOs, advising their counter-crime approaches. Yet the more time she spent in policy work, the more frustrated she became.

"I became completely exasperated that the tools I knew existed weren't being employed in the fight against human trafficking," she explained in an interview with *Forbes*.[85] It was an infuriating disconnect: on the one hand, cutting-edge cyber intelligence techniques like image and video analysis; on the other, underfunded law enforcement agencies with tedious investigative practices.

The data was all *there*. Trafficking activity left its traces all over the Internet, but almost no one was gathering, analyzing, or taking action upon it. Many organizations—social services, government agencies, attorneys general—did collect data but, for privacy reasons or simply because of a lack of coordination, kept it "siloed" away from agencies that could make use of it. Meanwhile, perpetrators were getting away with brazen impunity. If only law enforcement agencies could efficiently extract meaningful information from these sources, they could pinpoint criminals with precision rather than grasping at wisps of clues too late.

Although not a technologist herself, Sherrie was aware of developments in the cyber intelligence space—particularly

---

2019).

85 Ibid.

because her husband Sergio worked as the Director of Threat Intelligence at Microsoft. She knew that technology had the potential to streamline anti-trafficking investigations. Then why was she still "having to pull up multiple screens to look into a phone number?"[86]

It bothered her, and she couldn't let it go.

She remembers, "I felt this really deep calling then, to do something about it and to marry those two worlds together."[87]

At the time, Sherrie was working as a policy advisor with the rescue organization Orphan Secure (now Freedom's Shield), a non-profit organization focused on equipping Latin American orphanages to counter child sex trafficking. That's where she began: sharing her vision with the law enforcement, intelligence, and military professionals involved with Orphan Secure, as well as with technologists that Sergio had worked with before. She wanted to build cutting-edge tools that would inform anti-trafficking operations and facilitate collaborative trust among stakeholders like policy makers, investigators, and non-profit leaders.

In March 2016, they had enough support to launch as a full-fledged NGO, with Sergio spearheading the technical details and Sherrie taking charge as Executive Director.

---

86 Magee, Tamlin. "Inside GEN, the nonprofit combatting human trafficking with big data." *Computerworld*, January 11, 2019. IDG Communications (September 28, 2019).

87 Thorpe, Devin. "The New Sheriff In Human Trafficking Is Wielding Big Data." *Forbes*, October 11, 2018. Forbes Media (September 28, 2019).

Sherrie tirelessly met with representatives from all sectors—tech corporations, government agencies, academics, policymakers, private businesses, NGOs—to create partnerships and raise the funds they needed. Meanwhile, her small cohort of volunteers began developing a versatile intelligence and data analytics platform, which they named Minerva after the Roman goddess of strategic warfare.

And Global Emancipation Network was born.

It was a small but dedicated team, to name a few: Justin Underwood, an intelligence analyst at Microsoft who had worked with Sergio and Sherrie at Orphan Secure; Geoff Freeman, another Microsoft employee; college students from the University of Portland, including my friend Christine Chen; Satoshi Kawasaki, a Splunk engineer who donated his time through his company's Splunk4Good program; and Emilia Vanderwerf, a stay-at-home mom who began volunteering with GEN during her transition back into full-time employment. Each volunteer came onboard eager to give their time and skills—and in some cases, bringing with them valuable networks of engineers and potential sponsors.

Creating Minerva wasn't easy by any means. Obviously, money was the main limiting factor. Before they had an operating budget, Sherrie personally financed the costs of the endeavor, and the work was done entirely by part-time volunteers located around the country. Over time, however, donations began to pour in. Generous funding from charitable foundations and other organizations even allowed some volunteers, including Emilia Vanderwerf, to transition to full-time positions.

And corporate partners donated their tech products: Microsoft supplied its Azure cloud computing software, Deep Vision AI provided its Visual Intelligence engine for face recognition services, and Splunk contributed its powerful data analytics platform, Splunk Enterprise, as part of its brand-new Splunk4Good pledge—just to name a few. During an email exchange with Emilia, she told me that there's a lot to learn: "the crawler, data pipeline, and Minerva website each have their own code bases; the databases Splunk and SQL also have many intricacies, and Microsoft Azure platform is a learning curve"—but these donated tools also enable them to harness technical power that they wouldn't otherwise be able to afford as a non-profit.

"We apply an analytic framework called the Human Trafficking Kill Chain," Sherrie says, explaining GEN's holistic approach to tackle human trafficking.[88] Essentially, they look at every stage in the trafficking process to expose opportunities for disruption, which include grooming victims, entrapping and transporting them, and advertising them online. Ideally, the goal would be to intervene as early as possible, thwarting exploitation before it even happens.

---

88 New, Joshua. "5 Q's for Sherrie Caltagirone, Executive Director of the Global Emancipation Network." *Data Innovation*, November 5, 2018. Center for Data Innovation, (September 28, 2019).

"Most of our volunteers have decades of experience hunting hackers and know the methods of detecting people trying to hide and then uncovering their operations," Sherrie explains.[89] These individuals "gather data on the open, deep, and dark web—whether it's an ad placed on an escort site [where traffickers advertise their victims' 'voluntary' services] or an H-1B visa blacklist," which lists U.S. companies guilty of employing foreign immigrants for meager salaries.[90]

Then, "we join text with public records data and enrich it with geospatial tools, natural language processing, and more," Sherries continues, "and process images [of people] through specialized image analysis tools to gain insights into…their age, gender, ethnicity, and other attributes."[91] Through the algorithms embedded in Minerva, they crawl through that data and send it through a pipeline to detect patterns that could offer clues to the activity of perpetrators and their victims.

Finally, GEN presents these findings in a dashboard designed to be accessible for users like law enforcement officers or attorneys general. "These users, who come from law

89 "theCube Interview with Sherrie Caltagirone." *Global Emancipation NGO*, September 26, 2017. Global Emancipation Network (September 28, 2019).

90 New, Joshua. "5 Q's for Sherrie Caltagirone, Executive Director of the Global Emancipation Network." *Data Innovation*, November 5, 2018. Center for Data Innovation, (September 28, 2019).

91 "theCube Interview with Sherrie Caltagirone." *Global Emancipation NGO*, September 26, 2017. Global Emancipation Network (September 28, 2019).

enforcement, government, academia, nonprofits, and the private sector, are also able to store and process their own trafficking data securely within Minerva and share that data at their discretion with other users within the ecosystem at varying levels of granularity," says Sherrie.[92]

To make it a little more concrete for me, Emilia described some scenarios when customers would be able to use Minerva. For example, if officials at the Los Angeles Police Department have "been assigned to investigate potential trafficking cases in their specific geographic area [but currently] have no leads," Minerva allows them to "do a broad search to browse through escort activity that is happening around LA." After looking through the results, they can then decide where to concentrate their energies.

If, on the other hand, law enforcement already has "a specific username, address, phone number, or set of keywords that are suspicious," they can type that information into Minerva's Google-like search bar "to search Minerva's database to see if Minerva has ads, reviews, threads, or user profiles associated with these search terms." Or, if an official has a recent photo of a missing child, they can "upload the photo through Minerva's upload tool, which runs facial recognition and age prediction algorithms on the person's face and returns all highest-rated matches of images already in

---

92 New, Joshua. "5 Q's for Sherrie Caltagirone, Executive Director of the Global Emancipation Network." *Data Innovation*, November 5, 2018. Center for Data Innovation, (September 28, 2019).

Minerva's database," to see if there are other images of the child that may give clues as to his or her whereabouts.

"The alerts can tell us not only that there is a problem," Sherrie explained, "but can begin to predict what might happen next."[93] That's going to be key in enabling law enforcement, social service agencies, researchers, private businesses, and other organizations to stop chasing the tails of traffickers and instead begin to gain the upper hand by anticipating their future movements. "Hopefully then," says Sherrie, "we can take action before a problem is present."[94]

Exceeding their own expectations, the Global Emancipation Network team celebrated Minerva's GA (general availability) release on September 24, 2018. Already, Minerva has been used to identify hundreds of thousands of victims, and over 989 individuals (including both traffickers and victims) have been referred to law enforcement action—and that's just from "a single, two-month investigation of a single U.S.-based website," Sherrie said.[95]

One day, Sherrie was contacted by a woman named Heather (pseudonym), a consensual sex worker who supplemented her day-job wages with her earnings at an escort

---

93 McDonald, Claire. "Machine data for good: How Splunk is partnering with firms to make the world a better place." *Computer Weekly*, November 16, 2017. TechTarget (September 28, 2019).

94 Ibid.

95 New, Joshua. "5 Q's for Sherrie Caltagirone, Executive Director of the Global Emancipation Network." *Data Innovation*, November 5, 2018. Center for Data Innovation, (September 28, 2019).

service. However, now she'd gotten entangled with a human trafficking ring. "She was completely panicked" when she realized they were planning to trap her, Sherrie remembers.[96] But with Minerva's help, Global Emancipation Network identified the individuals in the trafficking ring and reached out to organizations that could intervene in her case. "We were able to rescue her from that situation and she was not trafficked," Sherrie reported.[97] Heather's is just one of the many lives that have been assisted thanks to Global Emancipation Network.

Sherrie's already planning myriad other ways to target different areas of the Human Trafficking Kill Chain. Currently, GEN has partnered with organizations who are focused on intercepting the transportation of victims through international airports, border crossings, and refugee flows; health care providers who often interface with trafficking victims without realizing it; and other stakeholders in the private sector who want automated screening tools to help catch trafficking situations early on, before the exploitation even happens. "Once trafficking is considered as a data problem, data solutions begin to emerge," says Sherrie.[98] She's excited

---

96 Thorpe, Devin. "The New Sheriff In Human Trafficking Is Wielding Big Data." *Forbes*, October 11, 2018. Forbes Media (September 28, 2019).

97 Ibid.

98 New, Joshua. "5 Q's for Sherrie Caltagirone, Executive Director of the Global Emancipation Network." *Data Innovation*, November 5, 2018. Center for Data Innovation, (September 28, 2019).

to see where these projects take GEN as they work to uncover trafficker networks in all areas of their activity.

FROM THE SHADOWS TO THE SPOTLIGHT

Sherrie and her team are not alone in the fight. While Global Emancipation Network has a broad scope—combating "all forms of trafficking against men, women, and children all over the world," utilizing data from all kinds of websites that are more difficult to access, and making their tool freely available to any entity with a clear anti-trafficking mission (as opposed to just government agencies or law enforcement), other organizations have found their own niches in driving technological innovation to catch traffickers red-handed.[99]

One of these specifically targets child sexual exploitation. Co-founded by actor Ashton Kutcher in 2009, Thorn builds tools to reduce the amount of abusive content on online platforms, identify victim and buyer profiles, and transform data from the dark web into meaningful information for law enforcement.

For Kutcher, it began when he and his then-wife, Demi Moore, watched an exposé about the devastating scourge of child pornography and sex trafficking. "Children that were six and seven years old were being molested for money,"

---

99 Ibid.

Kutcher remembers.[100] As a father of two himself, he couldn't turn away from the atrocity. "I've been on FBI raids where I've seen things that no person should ever see…" he declared before Congress in February 2017. "I've seen things that make you question humanity."[101] From then on, he was committed to the cause, prepared to take it on for the rest of his life.

Digital child pornography has exploded over the past several years because of the increased communication that's possible over the Internet. "Traffickers no longer have to just work the street; they can just place an ad and sit back and have their customers come to them wherever they might be," Moore explains.[102] "People are posted and sold online multiple times a day," attests a teen sex trafficking survivor called Asia. "Just how you can go find a car, it was a picture and a description and a price" (Thorn 2013). What a sickening disregard of dignity—and yet, this kind of dehumanization is commonplace online. In fact, as of 2013, the United States was the number one producer of child pornography in the world, facilitated by vastly undercover online networks (Thorn 2013).

While it's horrible that technological advancements have enabled this crime to expand, it also provides an opportunity to intervene. The first step was bringing together people and resources—truly from all over. Julie Cordua, currently

---

100 "We are Thorn." *YouTube*, November 14, 2013. Thorn (September 28, 2019).
101 Ibid.
102 Ibid.

the executive director of Thorn, says that "the whole idea was to bring the brightest minds in technology together to brainstorm around this issue" (Thorn 2013). "One of the first things that Demi and Ashton did," she remembers, "was they built a technology task force," which is essentially a team of individuals and departments from different sectors to work together on a specific issue.[103]

From there, the alliances grew. They started with eight employees; now they have thirty-six, hoping to double that number over the next year.[104] Beyond the immediate members of the task force and the developer team, everyone who is now involved with Thorn in some way or another—as researchers, user testers, or fundraisers—each jumped on board at different times and for different reasons, all pouring their brainpower and energy together for the common goal of seeing children free and safe. "The name Thorn itself has a beautiful connotation," explains Jim Pitkow, director and chairman of the Thorn task force. "Thorns protect the rose, and the roses here are our children, and their futures."[105]

They call themselves Digital Defenders of Children, and they don't take their responsibility lightly.

103 Ibid.

104 O'Brien, Sara Ashley. "Ashton Kutcher's nonprofit gets boost to fight against child abuse on the internet." *CNN Business*, April 17, 2019. CNN (September 28, 2019).

105 "We are Thorn." *YouTube*, November 14, 2013. Thorn (September 28, 2019).

A large part of Thorn's work is performing analysis on sex ads in order to trace the activity to the perpetrators responsible for it, to help investigators pinpoint the whereabouts of victims. To make sense of the seeming randomness, Dr. Portnoff explains, "I'm writing code that will be able to take groups of ads and say whether or not these ads are connected to each other" by scanning them for similar writing styles.[106]

Thorn is probably most well-known for its product called Spotlight, which Kutcher describes as "a tool that can be used by law enforcement to prioritize their caseload."[107] Law enforcement doesn't have the time to navigate the data from the online commercial sex market, let alone try to gather meaningful conclusions from the overwhelming amount of information. That's where Spotlight comes in—pulling together publicly available data to make sense of it and then putting it in the hands of investigators so that they can make use of it.

One of the challenges is that traffickers posting advertisements naturally "want to disguise that information somehow, so that any of the girls don't appear to be minors, that these are all independent people working separately," says Rebecca Sorla Portnoff, who earned her PhD from UC Berkeley in 2017

---

106 "Activism 2.0: Coding against sex trafficking." *Berkeley News*, January 30, 2019. University of California, Berkeley (September 28, 2019).

107 "Ashton Kutcher Speech on Human Trafficking Before Congress." *YouTube*, February 15, 2017. ABC News (September 28, 2019).

and now works as a research and data scientist at Thorn.[108] They display numbers from "burner phones" as well as elusive email addresses, which minimizes the connection between their ads to dispel suspicion. Sometimes, the images they post are duplicitous too: Asia remembers that "there was a girl who eerily looked like me—that was the picture they put up there for me on the ad."[109]

Another strategy she uses is to examine bitcoin, a digital form of currency that lends itself to anonymous transactions. However, people who advertise and purchase pornography or sex from trafficking victims online might not be as untraceable as they think. In a bit of detective fashion, Dr. Portnoff compares bitcoin transaction times with the times that ads were posted, matching payment and posting times to connect an ad to the bitcoin wallet that was probably used to pay for it. "If we're able to say, hey these fifty ads that previously did not appear to be connected were actually all paid for by the same wallet, we now have a very strong definitive link connecting these ads together," she says. "Several of the wallets that we found spent 50,000, 60,000 even up to 100,000 dollars in just four weeks on paying for these ads, and that was shocking to see all of that money going in this direction."[110]

---

108 "Activism 2.0: Coding against sex trafficking." *Berkeley News*, January 30, 2019. University of California, Berkeley (September 28, 2019).
109 "We are Thorn." *YouTube*, November 14, 2013. Thorn (September 28, 2019).
110 Ibid.

Developed with the support of Arizona State University's McCain Institute as well as Tennessee-based company Digital Reasoning, whose engineers did pro bono work for Thorn, Spotlight has helped law enforcement expedite their identification of children who appear in sexually abusive material and locate the perpetrators who control them.

"It's a neural net," Kutcher explained. "It gets smarter over time, it gets better and it gets more efficient as people use it. And it's working."[111] It's currently being used by 1,400 agencies in all fifty states and Canada, and it's "helped in identifying 31,197 victims of human trafficking—9,380 of them children—and 10,496 traffickers in the past three years" … plus a reported sixty-three percent reduction in investigation time.[112]

"It's always one of the first places I check when I get a tip, and the related ads/phone number search is truly a lifesaver," a federal investigative analyst shared. "I was recently able to use Spotlight to help to identify a girl I had been working to identify for a few weeks. Most of her current ads were removed, so having the archive of ads and pictures in Spotlight was a huge help."[113]

---

111 "Ashton Kutcher Speech on Human Trafficking Before Congress." *YouTube*, February 15, 2017. ABC News (September 28, 2019).

112 "Spotlight Changes the Way Law Enforcement Investigates Sex Trafficking." *Spotlight*, 2019. Thorn and Digital Reasoning (September 28, 2019).

113 Ibid.

At the Bernalillo County Sheriff's Office in New Mexico, detectives Kyle Woods and Kyle Hartsock have also found Spotlight to be extremely useful in their investigations, "besides our old-fashioned cop work and interview skills."[114] As part of the county's Ghost Unit, they work on behalf of the "ghosts" in their society, searching for runaways, missing people, and victims of crime. Without Spotlight, they say that they "would have lost a significant amount of evidence, or it would have been such a greater task to get it from the websites."[115] This tool enables them to streamline their operations.

"We've used it to track a victim's movement across the country," they report, "with exact dates and times of posts as well as when phone numbers changed (the trafficker picked her up, etc.)." And Spotlight also comes in handy once the victims have been recovered, if they are reluctant or afraid to give information: "We use it in victim interviews, which can be the turning point where they realize we know too much and full denials just won't work anymore."[116] In another instance, the detectives were able to identify an ad that a child sex trafficker had posted six months earlier, which ultimately "cracked open the case and [led] to a successful prosecution."[117]

---

114 Woods, Kyle and Kyle Hartsock. "Using Spotlight to investigate human trafficking." *Thorn Blog*, August 9, 2018. Thorn (September 28, 2019).

115 Ibid.

116 Ibid.

117 Ibid.

Another time, Woods and Hartsock remember that "while working with the family of a runaway, the mother gave us a tip that we ran through Spotlight. With the information collected, we started to pinpoint identifying factors and heightened our response to locate this listed runaway" (Woods and Hartsock, 2018). Eventually, that information gave them the insight they needed to be able to rescue her and set her on the path to recovery. "She is now safe and with family...in inpatient services" they write, adding that they're using Spotlight to continue their investigation.[118]

Now *that's* an impact!

It's amazing to see how technology can be used to shine a light on trafficking activity that was once undercover. With the Slavery from Space project uncovering sites of possible forced labor in brick kilns, stone quarries, and cotton fields, and tools like Spotlight and Minerva identifying sexual exploitation on the dark web, we'll be able to root out slavery where it lurks in the most evasive places.

Developing these technologies sends a message to victims that we haven't forgotten them, that we will do whatever it takes to locate them. It gives law enforcement the timely information they need to intervene. And it warns traffickers that we *see* them. We hold them accountable.

And we *will* bring them to justice.

---

118 Ibid.

CHAPTER 5:

DERAIL THE DEMAND

"If we do not create effective solutions to curb demand among solicitors just as we do to intervene among traffickers, we will not be able to really stop the problem."

—ANNALISA ENRILE, VICE-CHAIR OF THE DEPARTMENT OF SOCIAL CHANGE AND INNOVATION AT THE USC SUZANNE DWORAK-PECK SCHOOL OF SOCIAL WORK[119]

Because human trafficking flourishes as a commercial operation, it makes sense that the standard rules of supply and demand would apply. While the previous chapter discussed ways people are using technology to target

---

119 "How Demand Impacts Human Trafficking Statistics on a Global Scale." *USC Suzanne Dowark-Peck News,* January 18, 2019. USC Suzanne Dworak-Peck School of Social Work (September 28, 2019).

the supply side of the crime, such as interfering with the traffickers' activity, we can also take steps to reduce the number of people exploited by decreasing the demand for their services.

Oftentimes, consumers don't give a thought to the source of whatever they're purchasing—whether that's sex from a woman who supposedly chose this as her career or the new T-shirt, chocolate, or video game gadget in their shopping cart without thinking about the people who harvested, crafted, and packaged these products. Even conscious consumers find it difficult to trace items back to the labor that produced them, free or otherwise. However, with intentional disruption via technology, we can expose the forced sex and forced labor behind these goods and services, redirecting buyers to more ethical ways of living and ultimately decreasing the motivation to exploit other humans for profit.

SOMEBODY'S WATCHING

One of the most powerful ways technology is currently being leveraged to stifle the demand that fuels human trafficking is through disruption of online searches to buy sex. With so many commercial sex transactions occurring over the Internet, it's a prime space for individuals who feel invisible behind a screen.

"People can search to buy sex from a trafficking victim, set up an appointment and be able to meet them in an hour and a half, forty-five minutes," says Robert Beiser, executive director of Seattle Against Slavery.[120] In fact, according to the Washington-based alliance Businesses Ending Slavery and Trafficking (BEST), the rate of soliciting sex peaks around 2 p.m.... while these individuals are still at work.[121] Their spouses, their co-workers, their neighbors—even an acquaintance randomly passing on the street—would have no idea what they're up to as they discreetly arrange a rendezvous with an often underage girl.

When I learned about this reality, it devastated me. How many seemingly upstanding people had I encountered who had bought sex from a stranger who was probably forced or coerced against her will?

Indeed, "The offenders in these kinds of crimes do not match society's stereotype," explains Ernie Allen, President and CEO of the International Centre for Missing and Exploited Children. "These are people who are part of our community."[122]

I'd always assumed that no one in *my* professional or social circles would stoop to that kind of activity, but now I realized it could be *anyone.*

---

120 Mirfendereski, Taylor. "Seattle nonprofit takes on sex buyers with technology." *K5 News*, November 8, 2017. KING-TV (September 28, 2019).

121 Brettmann, Mar and Sandip Soli. "Sex Trafficking is Bad For Businesses." *BEST Alliance*, September 10, 2015. Businesses Ending Slavery & Trafficking (September 28, 2019).

122 "We are Thorn." *YouTube*, November 14, 2013. Thorn (September 28, 2019).

Angie Holbrook, a woman who spent the summer of 2018 hiking the Pacific Crest Trail to fundraise for Thorn, experienced this devastation firsthand. The reason she was involved with Thorn was because child sex trafficking thrust itself into her life from the place she least expected: her husband. "My world fell apart," she remembered. "My ex wasn't a shady felon, an angry alcoholic, or anything in between"—and yet she "found private messages that were sent to him in which the sender included pictures of a young girl, promising that she was fourteen, even though she 'looked older.'"[123] She could not get those images out of her mind. "Finding the CSAM [Commercial Sexual Abuse of a Minor] in his account," Holbrook said, "made me realize that if it was happening under my roof, and I had no idea, it was probably a much larger epidemic than I could ever imagine."[124]

Unfortunately, she was right. In fact, it's such a widespread—and invisible—problem that James Dinkins, Executive Associate Director of ICE Homeland Security Investigations (HSI), admits, "It's really impossible for law enforcement to deal with this issue alone. We can't arrest our way out of it."[125]

Even if we could arrest everyone who was guilty, where would that leave our society? Would this top-down pressure from law enforcement be enough to squelch the demand for

123 Holbrook, Angie. "Angie Holbrook: Why I fundraise for Thorn." *Thorn Blog*, November 8, 2018. Thorn (September 28, 2019).

124 Ibid.

125 "We are Thorn." *YouTube*, November 14, 2013. Thorn (September 28, 2019).

purchased sex, or would it only chase it into other, more clandestine, pathways?

What if, instead, we could influence a cultural change by challenging the mindset that buying sex is okay?

"This is an intersectional social justice issue that has to do with class, race, sex discrimination," Liz Rush told me. We can take advantage of technology to help open people's eyes "to the exploitation that happens when people buy sex. Yes, there are some consensual sex workers, but the majority are victims in some form or another."

That's why Thorn, the organization co-founded by Ashton Kutcher to fight child sexual exploitation, develops software that recognizes when someone is searching for sex or engaging with child pornographic material online, and triggers a pop-up message on the search engine which says, "WE KNOW WHERE YOU ARE. If we can find you, so can the police." It explains the legal consequences of interacting with images of sexually exploited children—up to thirty years in jail plus a lifetime listing on the Sex Offender Registry—and then urges the user to click the button to "Get help, before you get arrested."[126]

The grassroots NGO Seattle Against Slavery also focuses a large portion of its efforts on buyer deterrence as part of their Freedom Signal tech platform. "When we were looking at what interventions would be necessary to get people to stop

---

126 Ibid.

buying trafficked sex," says executive director Robert Beiser, "it was going online and disrupting the pathway where people have such an easy time exploiting others."[127] Again, a digital problem lends itself to a digital solution.

Like Thorn, SAS began experimenting with tech-enabled buyer deterrence in February 2014, running over two million ads on local search engine results in Washington State counties. When someone searches for terms that indicate they might be looking to buy sex, such as "teen escort," they might see an ad that says something like, *Want to buy sex, but don't want that horrible feeling of regret afterward? This time, make a decision that will help you instead of hurt you.*[128] When someone clicks on the ad, they're redirected to a website where they find information about how buying sex is really harmful to the individuals on the other side of it, as well as to the buyers themselves.

Since then, Seattle Against Slavery has expanded its impact by running fifteen-second videos on Facebook and Instagram in June 2016. Instead of directly responding to specific search terms in Internet browsers, the videos appear in the user's social media feed, stopping them in their tracks with brief vignettes about the real consequences of buying sex. Because of this targeted strategy, Robert said the social

---

127 "Why Focus On Sex Buyers?." *YouTube*, September 19, 2017. KING 5 News (September 28, 2019).

128 Mirfendereski, Taylor. "Seattle nonprofit takes on sex buyers with technology." *K5 News*, November 8, 2017. KING-TV (September 28, 2019).

media approach "is maybe a little bit more upstream" because it reaches people who aren't actively looking to book a sex appointment at that exact moment.[129] Based on their online activity, there's a good chance they're interested in that kind of content. It can throw them off their guard.

Another even more unsettling disruption for buyers are the decoy chatbots Seattle Against Slavery developed to model different profiles of potential victims (they're currently working on their first male profile.) A bot poses as either a minor or an adult and interacts with buyers through a fake phone number, so the buyers think they're texting a real person. After mimicking realistic texting patterns like misspelling, emojis, and delaying a response in an artificial intelligence language designed by survivors, the bot cleverly gets the buyer to share information such as their location, their age, employer, and intent—including whether they'd be okay with buying sex from a minor. Then, the bot will reveal its true colors and warn the buyer about the legal consequences of buying trafficked sex. In addition, the chatbot can redirect the buyer to a website where they can access resources for help to stop buying sex.

At SAS's fundraiser in October 2018, Liz Rush gave a rundown of how their multi-faceted Freedom Signal technology can make an impact. When a buyer opens his Facebook feed and sees a clip of a man behind bars with the caption,

---

129 Ibid.

The moment they put those cuffs on, I knew my secret was out... and he hops over to Instagram only to find another video which says, *How much did buying sex cost? I can't go to my son's birthday party because I'm a registered sex offender,* it can be disturbing and confusing.[130] Later, when the buyer starts a text conversation with the girl he's planning to meet that night, she—who is actually a bot—warns him he could end up spending time in jail or facing a huge fine. It starts to seem like *somebody's watching.*

When anonymity is threatened, behavior begins to shift.

"We know that we are targeting the right men because a lot of the men respond and comment back and get into arguments with the ads [in the comments]," Robert said.[131] Law enforcement has also seen success with using the bots as a preliminary tactic to set up stings to apprehend high-risk buyers. But the thing is, "Most of the men who said they bought sex in the last year have also said they want to stop."[132] The men are not only harming the victims, but they're also harming themselves. So, Seattle Against Slavery makes sure their deterrence is always linked to resources where these men can find support to change their habits, such as weekly classes or counseling groups. "We can shift the dialogue," says Robert.[133]

---

130 Ibid.
131 Ibid.
132 Ibid.
133 Ibid.

It's working: as of 2017, they've seen a twenty percent drop in the number of people searching for sex online in the Greater Seattle Area.[134] When I talked with Robert in January 2019, he mentioned SAS compared these statistics to other cities of comparable size and demographics and found this steep drop-off is a trend that is unique to Seattle. That seems to indicate the buyer deterrence strategies are contributing to this decline in demand!

"Technology gave us the ability to do that," said Robert, "in a way that would be very hard to do in the real world, you know, like putting up a billboard, or putting up a sign on the side of a bus."

As the demand decreases, hopefully the number of sex trafficking victims will as well.

AN APP IS NOT ALWAYS THE ANSWER

In some sense, shifting the demand for commercial sex, which drives sex trafficking, is "easier" than shifting the demand for the goods and services produced with labor trafficking. Robert Beiser says when it comes to the sexual exploitation of victims for someone else's profit, "It's totally voluntary, and it can stop, and all we need to do is get [these individuals] to stop buying sex."[135] However, labor traffick-

---

134 Rosoff, Henry. "Using memes, Facebook videos and Google adds to combat sex trafficking." *KIRO 7*, April 12, 2017. Cox Media Group (September 28, 2019).

135 Mirfendereski, Taylor. "Seattle nonprofit takes on sex buyers with technology." *K5 News*, November 8, 2017. KING-TV (September 28,

ing involves a dauntingly convoluted supply chain. With our present systems, it's nearly impossible for the average consumer to discern whether forced labor was involved in the process. And unlike in the sex trafficking scene, we can't simply stop purchasing the items that we need to live, such as clothes, fruit, and technological devices that enable us to communicate with our coworkers and friends.

As globalization expands the scale of massive corporations, supply chain transparency is becoming ever more important, yet ever more difficult to trace. On the one hand, we have seen an increase in initiatives to purchase products that are marked with certain labels denoting that they are ethically sourced. Including FairTrade, Equal Exchange, and Fair for Life, these labels indicate that their products are free from discriminatory hiring practices and abusive labor conditions. They are meant to empower consumers to support companies that uphold an ethical business model.

On the other hand, in order to acquire these labels, companies must undergo costly procedures to ensure that workers at every step of the supply chain are contributing their hours on their own initiative, have the freedom to leave their job if they wanted to, are treated decently, and receive their entitled wages.[136] The difficulty in acquiring these certifications hurts small businesses that want to maintain an ethical

---

2019).
136 "Fair Trade Standards." *Fair Trade Certified*, 2019. Fair Trade USA (September 28, 2019).

supply chain but don't have the capacity to prove it to customers. It also means that consumers who want to buy products made with dignified labor are faced with a confusing mess of semi-reliable labels that are still unable to tell the whole story. It's not uncommon for a label indicating "fair labor" to naively mask the exploitation that still occurs behind the packaging; the stamp is only a symbol, not a guarantee.

In the past years, many people have attempted to curb labor trafficking through consumer influence, by way of apps that can be downloaded onto personal mobile devices. "In 2018, there were more than fifty anti-slavery apps available in Apple and Google's app stores," notes slavery expert Catharina Drejer. "Some apps allow you to report observed or experienced slavery, some give you advice and guidance, others give you information about slavery and some focus on access to value chains."[137] By increasing people's access to information, tech developers hope that these apps will adjust spending habits accordingly, which will in turn pressure companies to rigorously eliminate forced labor at every point in their supply chains.

Let's take a look at a few of these apps and the way they have attempted to tackle human trafficking by influencing consumer behavior.

---

137 Drejer, Catharina. "«Tech for good» på sårbares bekostning [at the expense of the vulnerable]." *Skaperkraft*, January 25, 2019. Tankesmien Skaperkraft (September 28, 2019; translation).

Developed by an Italian company called Molleindustria and released in 2011, Phone Story is perhaps the consumer-focused app that highlights most exclusively the issue of forced labor, as opposed to overall sustainability and ethics. "The story was meant to generate some discussion about hardware and our socioeconomic impact as consumers of electronics," said Paolo Pedercini, a game designer from Carnegie Mellon University who headed the production of the app.[138] To that end, it's designed as a game that guides players through the manufacturing process of technological devices. Pedercini planned to have players experience four different scenarios: (1) mining the "conflict mineral" coltan in the Congo, a mineral found in all smartphones; (2) outsourcing labor in China, including the Foxconn factory notorious for employee suicides; (3) e-waste in Pakistan; and (4) gadget consumerism in the West.

Needless to say, Phone Story is anything but entertaining, with its unflinching depictions provoking "a critical reflection [of the smartphone device] on its own technological platform."[139] Within a system of planned obsolescence, many people don't give a second thought to the *who*, *what*, or *where* behind their latest smartphone or game console. "We don't want people to stop buying smartphones," Pedercini said,

138 Wortham, Jenna. "Game That Critiques Apple Vanishes From App Store." *Bits*, September 13, 2011. The New York Times Company (September 28, 2019).

139 "About Phone Story." *Phone Story*, 2019. Molleindustria (September 28, 2019).

"but maybe we can make a little contribution in terms of shifting the perception of technological lust from cool to not-that-cool."[140] If we can temper the constant demand for new hardware, and if we can adjust our priorities to care more about the workers who assemble our devices rather than the devices themselves, we'll be making strides toward improving labor conditions in that industry.

Where can you find the Phone Story app? It's currently available for Android devices, but it has definitely met its share of opposition: Apple banned Phone Story from the iTunes store just three hours after Pedercini began promoting it on Twitter. Although Apple claimed that the app's disturbing representations of abuse violated their policies and that Molleindustria could not donate the proceeds from their app to charitable organizations, it is also undeniable that this tech giant would not be pleased with an app that satirized their own business model—including Apple's partnership with the manufacturing company Foxconn. Justified or not, however, the app and the controversy surrounding it did arouse public awareness of the issue via media attention.

Many other, less controversial, apps are designed to empower consumers to alter their shopping habits in order to support brands that are ethically sourced. These include DoneGood, Co-Go, and Buycott, all of which allow consumers to select the criteria that matter to them. One person

---

140 Hick, Melanie. "Apple Bans Anti-iPhone Game App." *Huffington Post*, November 14, 2011. Verizon Media (September 28, 2019).

may choose to filter their search results for products that are eco-friendly and free from animal cruelty. Another person might want to make sure they support companies that pay their workers a living wage and do not employ children. Then, these users can easily find products that align with their values, sending conscious cues to businesses that they care about what happens behind the scenes. Basically, the idea is that an informed consumer is an empowered consumer.

While these apps don't focus exclusively on human trafficking, they help consumers situate this cause among the host of other concerning issues in our world today. In steering us away from products that are likely made with forced labor as well as notifying businesses of our purchasing choices, these apps can act as a first step toward the systemic changes in supply chain practices, enforcement of legislation, and our consumer culture in general that will need to occur in order to eradicate modern-day slavery for good.

It all sounds great on paper... but in practice it's not so straightforward. Simply put, the sheer number of apps doesn't correspond with actual improvement in the fight against human trafficking. That's why Catherina Drejer calls these apps *apparently* good. "I say 'apparently,'" she explains, "because it is not certain what effect the app has on slavery. This is difficult to measure... one cannot guarantee that the intended effect actually takes place."[141]

---

141 Drejer, Catharina. "«Tech for good» på sårbares bekostning [at the expense of the vulnerable]." *Skaperkraft*, January 25, 2019.

Thus, we have to be careful lest we fall into the mindset that an app has the power to solve all our problems. "That is rarely the case," Drejer states.[142] Even if it's a well-designed app, the pertinent challenge is gathering enough users so that it leads to visible change. Especially in an area like anti-trafficking work, where resources are precious, we must "ask whether the app is relevant and whether it will reach the intended users."[143] The last thing we want is to spend time, skill, and funding on a project that will soon enough fall flat on its face.

If no one uses the app, was it worth it?

According to Phil Bennett, the senior Salesforce program architect who now pours his energies full-time into advising anti-trafficking efforts, an app by itself is not the ticket to impact. In fact, that tunnel vision is often the reason for so many failed tech projects in the anti-trafficking space. Unfortunately, Phil notes that it's become easy and cheap to deploy poor-quality technology quickly. If you look at app stores, "there are lots of mobile apps trying to raise awareness about trafficking or slavery," he says, "but a lot of these just haven't gotten traction. People haven't downloaded them." The only individuals who *have* downloaded them are the ones who already know about human trafficking, so the developers

Tankesmien Skaperkraft (September 28, 2019; translation).
142 Ibid.
143 Ibid.

didn't reach their goal of raising awareness and educating the public.

When it comes down to it, "tech by itself is not good enough," as Phil says. Instead? We must "wrap the app." Phil explained this phrase to me: in order for an app to truly make an impact, it needs to be strategically funded and promoted so that more and more people use it as a commonplace platform. "You've got to wrap it in marketing, training, management, a network of people promoting it across organizations and sectors such as hospitals, police, other sectors," he said. "It's not just the app...you're changing *behaviors*". To do that, we need to engage a large-scale, collaborative campaign; it requires so much more than simply uploading a new technology package to the app store.

It doesn't mean that we should discard the idea of developing an app, but we must recognize that it is only *part* of the solution.

Phil pointed out that an overwhelming number of apps available in app stores may actually "dilute the potential impact of the few very good apps," deterring users from contributing to real change. "If a person is motivated to download an app to tackle trafficking, then how do they pick the best from the worst?" Phil asked. "Consumer reviews aren't always a reliable indicator. Also, very old apps might not be maintained properly." Other concerns around security, data collection, and privacy mean that many existing apps have questionable impacts.

That's not to say that if an anti-trafficking app doesn't take the world by storm, it is utterly pointless. However, we'll need to invest the resources to make sure the app upholds security and privacy standards, is maintained consistently, and is promoted effectively so that it will have the userbase necessary for a real impact.

There's so much more potential in this space: first, we can bolster the influence of existing anti-slavery apps by using them to inform our spending habits as well as sharing them with our social and professional networks. We can also create new apps with an intentional eye, collaborating with a variety of civic and corporate partners to ensure that the technology is integrated into everyday use. Lastly, we can look for ways that apps or other tech initiatives could be designed to decrease the demand for other forms of labor trafficking, such as hiring restaurant employees, salon staff, or nannies for little to no pay.

NO LONGER OUT OF SIGHT

Off the coast of Thailand, a small technological device is helping to increase transparency in the fishing industry, thereby reducing the vulnerability of fishermen to exploitation and ultimately, hopefully, allowing consumers to confidently purchase seafood free from forced labor. Recently, I had the chance to chat with Bangkok-based lawyer Dornnapha Sukkree about a promising new project that's gaining traction on Thai waters—not among high-profile law enforcement agencies or non-profit organizations but actually integrated among the community members who are directly impacted by labor trafficking.

Although Thailand is not alone in evincing labor abuses at sea—slavery on fishing vessels has been reported in countries such as the United States, China, Taiwan, Indonesia, Vietnam—its multibillion-dollar seafood industry has been most exposed to media and political scrutiny in recent years, especially since Thailand is one of the leading exporters of seafood to the United States. Migrant workers, usually from Cambodia and Indonesia, are attracted to jobs on Thai fishing boats for the chance to earn a living and support their families back home.[144] Once onboard, however, these men are confined offshore for months or years at a time in brutal conditions, all while accruing thousands of dollars of unpaid wages.

Dorna Sukkree told me that although she had practiced law for years, it wasn't until 2014 when a news report first gripped her attention to the plight of trafficked fishermen in her country. Out at sea, there's little that authorities can do to enforce regulations, so labor abuses are rampant: long hours, verbal and physical harassment, swindled wages, lack of food and sleep—and all of it unfolds in isolation, with no escape except for jumping into the sea. According to a man from Myanmar who spent eleven years enslaved on a Thai

---

144 "2018 Findings: Fishing." *Global Slavery Index*, 2018. The Walk Free Foundation (September 28, 2019).

fishing vessel, "it was like a floating prison—actually, worse than prison."[145]

"The abuse and exploitation of workers in the Thai fishing industry had been Thailand's worst-kept secret for years," said Sunai Phasuk, senior researcher for the international NGO Human Rights Watch.[146] However, even after international exposure in 2014 compelled Thailand's government to implement reforms addressing Illegal, Unreported, and Unregulated (IUU) Fishing, the exploitation is still as widespread as ever.

It's a common misconception that there are "no viable solutions for an enormous ocean full of small boats."[147] How could authorities possibly keep tabs on every single fishing vessel? How could they make sure that every fish is caught ethically, upholding labor rights?

"I [felt] so bad," Dorna said, "because... I realized that there were a lot of problems about human trafficking that I did not have any chance to help with... I [was] working in a law firm and did not have the ability to work pro bono." She decided to start her own legal consulting firm, which gave

---

145 Yi, Beh Lih and Rina Chandran. "Thailand banks on tech to end slavery at sea as workers push for rights." *Reuters*, June 19, 2018. Thomson Reuters Foundation (September 28, 2019).

146 "Thailand: Forced Labor, Trafficking Persist in Fishing Fleets." *Human Rights Watch News*, January 23, 2018. Human Rights Watch (September 28, 2019).

147 Garren, Melissa. "Technology to Fill Data Gaps at Sea." *International Conservation*, September 14, 2016. International Conservation Caucus Foundation (September 28, 2019).

her the independence to decide where and when she worked. Now she was able to focus her energies into her passion: fighting forced labor on fishing vessels.

From there, she began to initiate conversations with local NGOs about what they could do to combat "the root causes of human trafficking and IUU fishing in the Southeast Asia fishing sector with a collaborative, constructive approach."[148] Discussion turned to action. "We started a coalition in early 2016," Dornappha said. That's how she became the executive director of MAST, or the Multi-Stakeholder Initiative for Accountable Supply Chain of Thai Fisheries.

As a coalition, MAST facilitates coordination among stakeholders such as the Thai government and corporations, advocating for justice, labor rights, and sustainability in the fishing industry. "We act on behalf of fishers, we act on behalf of victims," Dorna stresses. "We want to have a solution from the bottom-up instead of top-down, international pressures." Although MAST connects with businesses, governments, policymakers, field experts, consumers, etc., their priority is serving and empowering the fisher communities themselves, focusing specifically on Myanmar and Thailand.

Soon, an exciting partnership opened up for a possible "bottom-up" solution: using technology to keep track of fishing vessels while they were at sea, to monitor their movement.

---

148 "MAST Human: A Nonprofit Combating Human Trafficking at Seas." *MAST Human* (September 28, 2019).

It seemed like an opportunity that could benefit everyone involved.

Two years earlier, a brilliant team of entrepreneurs in San Francisco—Pelagic Data Systems—had developed a data collection system to support supply chain transparency out at sea. The main piece of their system's hardware is a lightweight device that's about the size of a smartphone: waterproof, durable, and completely solar-powered. Once installed on a vessel, it records the vessel's location multiple times per minute. Then, whenever it enters mobile phone coverage range, the data is securely uploaded to a cloud platform where it's stored for data analysis and visualization on a user-friendly dashboard.

MAST reached out to Pelagic at the perfect time. Ready to test out their system, Pelagic's Chief Scientific Officer Melissa Garren said that she and her team were "thrilled for this opportunity to collaborate with our local partners on a focused project that will further refine and strengthen our solutions."[149] As the location to deploy the first pilot, Dorna "picked [a small fishery] in Prachuap Khiri Khan... [a province] about 120 miles away from Bangkok," a community that had impressed her by their commitment to sustainable fishery management as well as their strong social structure. This was important because they wanted the initiative to be

---

149 "NatGeo Marine Protection Prize Press Release." *Pelagic Data*, June 8, 2018. Pelagic Data Systems (September 28, 2019).

fisher-driven, with the community enforcing and monitoring the solution.

By the end of 2017, the pilot was fully underway. After installation of Pelagic's device on ten fishing vessels in Prachuap Khiri Khan, everything else—from the data collection to the uploading and analysis of results—was done automatically. This makes it extremely easy for the fishermen; as fishing is one of the most demanding jobs there is, MAST and Pelagic didn't want to add anything to the fishermen's daily routine. To further support the fishermen, members of the Pelagic team traveled to the province on a regular basis to check the equipment and communicate with the locals about how everything was going.

"At the time we had limited funding, so we had only ten [devices]," Dorna told me. Within the next few months, however, Melissa Garren and her team won the National Geographic Society-sponsored Marine Protection Prize, enabling them to enlarge the project to 100 devices.[150] And that's just the beginning.

So far, the fisher community has taken tremendous ownership of the technology. "They love it because… it's an incentive to work, to monitor what happens in the seas," Dorna told me. As for labor conditions aboard, there's still work to be done before the vessel-tracking device can actually play a role in identifying cases of forced labor. Of course,

---

150 Ibid.

fisheries that are violating regulations would not volunteer to install a location-tracker on their vessels. Right now, the goal is to collect data on "normal" fishing patterns—including where vessels are traveling, where they're stopping, and how they interact with other vessels nearby. Hopefully, this will lay a baseline foundation that they can later use to detect labor infractions.

By enhancing their ability to prove the sustainability of their operations, Pelagic's platform could also enable smaller fisheries to acquire the fair trade certifications that make them more attractive to customers who purchase seafood farther down the line. Together—with technology matching conscientious consumers to ethically sourced products—the communities at either end of the supply chain can work together toward an economy free from slavery.

CHAPTER 6:

REACH OUT TO VICTIMS

"[Technology has] actually made it easier for us to reach more victims of trafficking than it was before."

—AMANDA HIGHTOWER, EXECUTIVE DIRECTOR OF
REAL ESCAPE FROM THE SEX TRADE (REST)[151]

Besides disrupting perpetrators of human trafficking or deterring buyers of slave-sourced services, there's another prong of anti-trafficking work where technology can play a part: intervening in situations of possible exploitation to connect with victims themselves. The most effective solutions are integrated into technology that's already being already used by victims, such as text messages or Facebook accounts.

---

151 Lee, Dave. "The chatbot taking on Seattle's sex trade." *BBC News,* November 25, 2017. BBC (September 28, 2019).

When designing technology that reaches victims directly, it's of utmost importance to understand their experience in order to develop systems that will be safe, scalable, and sensitive to their needs. Survivor input is an absolute must—after all, they're the experts in the terrain, knowing what will be most impactful... or what may actually lead to more harm. Antislavery expert Catharina Drejer explains, "[Survivors] have unique insight into what could prevent their situation and have important thoughts about, for example, these long-term consequences."[152] Even if something seems like a great idea from a technologist's point of view, the survivors could point out flaws that no one else would be aware of.

That's why close collaboration with survivors and on-the-ground organizations is crucial!

BEFREE

"Why can't you receive texts? I would have texted you."

Since December 2007, the nongovernmental organization Polaris Project had managed the United States' National Human Trafficking Hotline, which had operated as a toll-free number available 24/7 in 200 languages, connecting an expansive network of anti-trafficking resources. Anyone in the United States can call in to report a tip for a possible

---

152 Drejer, Catharina. "Blockchain-teknologi kan brukes mot slaveri. Men vi kjenner ikke alle konsekvensene [Blockchain technology can be used against slavery. But we do not know all the consequences]." *Skaperkraft*, November 19, 2018. Tankesmien Skaperkraft (September 28, 2019; translation).

trafficking situation they've seen, or if they need help themselves, the hotline will direct them to anti-trafficking services in their area. Yet Executive Director and CEO Bradley Myles remembers that they heard many people explaining why they didn't reach out for help, either former victims or individuals who had witnessed potential trafficking situations. "I might not have been comfortable calling you, because I didn't want to have someone overhear my conversation," they said.[153] "But, if I could have sent you a private silent text, I would have done that."[154]

This feedback prompted the Polaris Project to partner with Thorn, the organization driving technological innovation against child sex trafficking and sexual exploitation. Thanks to the work of Thorn's engineers, integrating software from both Twilio (for the SMS message delivery) and Salesforce (for powering their database with a service cloud framework), Polaris Project was able to accommodate its users' needs by launching a text shortcode in 2013. Now, in addition to calling a phone number, people also have the option to text their concerns to "BeFree" (233733). It's made a tremendous difference! Myles said, "We're already seeing examples of getting people out of modern-day slavery because of this text shortcode."[155]

---

153 "We are Thorn." *YouTube*, November 14, 2013. Thorn (September 28, 2019).
154 Ibid.
155 Ibid.

Here's how it could work: If you encounter someone you suspect might be in a trafficking situation, you discreetly pass them the phone number on a slip of paper. You tell them, "Hey, I don't know what your situation is, but if you ever feel like you need help, here's a number that you can contact." That person saves the number under a fake name in their phone, avoiding the suspicion of their traffickers. They can decide to text the hotline on their own time, when they are ready to reach out for help, and when they can send a message without their trafficker noticing. Staff members who manage the hotline will respond immediately, sending support and resources to help them leave that life.

These are simple uses of technology that we often take for granted: making a phone call or sending a quick text message. But for many survivors, it becomes a lifeline to freedom. Sometimes texting works. Sometimes they might be more comfortable on social media. In any case, we should tailor our methods of victim outreach depending on their specific needs, recognizing that ultimately it's not about the intervention itself but the relationship between survivors and advocates that can develop because of it.

REACHING VICTIMS FOR REST

One stellar example of victim-centered technology is Victim Outreach, a proactive texting feature that's part of the Freedom Signal platform developed by Seattle Against Slavery in partnership with several local organizations that support sex workers and survivors of sex trafficking. One of these part-ner organizations is called Real Escape from the Sex Trade (REST), a service provider in Seattle that offers a safe place for individuals in the sex trade to access the resources they need as they make the difficult transition out of "the life."

Jackie Loos, who is currently REST's Community Advo-cate Supervisor, is actually a survivor herself, having spent years in the sex trade. "One date turned into thousands of dates a year to make money for the man I loved, who was not only my boyfriend but my pimp," she says.[156] After meeting a REST employee who invited her to see what it was all about, she began to regularly attend their survivor support group called Thrive. "This was a place like no other," she remembers. "It was finally a space that was completely accepting, with-out judgment."[157] Amidst REST's services, which included trauma counseling, case management, and access to medical and mental health care, she found a home where she had the space and support she needed to heal.

When, a couple months later, Jackie learned that REST was looking for staff members to help run a new shelter, she applied without hesitation. Starting as a Peer Support Specialist, she was able to walk alongside survivors in their journeys, con-necting with them and supporting them in a "purely relational role." She was eager to reach out to these women who had been

---

156 "REST Survivors." Real Escape from the Sex Trade (September 28, 2019).
157 Ibid.

through similar experiences, in the same compassionate way that the other REST employee had done for her.

When I called her on the phone during what turned out to be a busy day at the REST shelter, Jackie told me when she first heard about the idea of automatic text outreach. Seattle Against Slavery and some volunteers from Microsoft had this dream… It was still in the fledgling stages, but they were starting to work together to develop software that would scan through sex ads online and scrape the phone numbers of potential victims of sex trafficking or commercial sexual exploitation. Then, service providers could send out text messages to hundreds of potential victims at once, letting them know that there are resources available if they want to get out of "the life."

Because of the force, fraud, or coercion that perpetrators use to control their victims, oftentimes victims of sex trafficking will not accept help right away. They might have been deceived into a twisted dependence on their trafficker, or they could be too afraid to try to escape because of what he or she has threatened to do if they did not behave. Victims also become so convinced of their worthlessness that hope feels too far away. Freedom is a foreign concept; they are beyond redemption. It takes "a trustworthy and consistent relationship to give someone the courage to walk away from their trafficker," REST explains on their website.[158] That's

---

158 "Our Programs: REST Principles of Care." *I Want Rest*, 2019. Real Escape from the Sex Trade (September 28, 2019).

their mission: to offer the kind of supportive relationship that many victims have never experienced in their lives.

Although her mom had worked for Microsoft for years, Jackie herself didn't know much about technical development. However, she did know how powerful this new technology from Seattle Against Slavery could be. Such a victim outreach platform could allow REST to reach many more individuals than they could hope to ever meet simply by walking the streets. "I'm a collaborative worker," she told me, adding with a laugh that she considers herself a "Jackie of all trades." So she jumped on the opportunity to work with SAS and Microsoft volunteers to make this idea a reality.

They really started rolling in the summer of 2016, at a Microsoft hackathon where tech employees set aside their day jobs to spend a week innovating ideas to solve some of the world's most pressing problems. During the event, REST and SAS pitched their project to the volunteers, explaining their vision for text outreach to victims. "After a successful pitch, dozens of Microsoft employees joined our Hack for Good team and begun helping us leverage our existing technology in order to improve our efficiency, accuracy, and scalability of our approach to outreach," the REST team wrote on their blog.[159]

"It's easy to get lost in our 'day jobs,' to stay heads-down in product launches and feature developments," says Danielle,

159 "We've Begun Our Year with a Real Game Changer." *REST News*, October 9, 2016. Real Escape from the Sex Trade (September 28, 2019).

a Microsoft employee who worked on REST's hackathon team and was so impacted by the experience that she wrote a letter to REST afterward. "In this, we're poking our heads into the light."[160] At the end of the week, their project was awarded first place in the Hack for Good category. But the momentum continued beyond that: "Many of those employees have continued to dedicate volunteer time to continue to enhance our project."[161] Since then, they've been able to unleash a dynamic symbiosis of technical expertise and on-the-ground impact through intentional collaboration.

At first, Jackie would send out about 150 texts a week, using Google Voice, a platform for managing telephone services including calls, voicemails, and texts. Originally, the text outreach platform was very simple: Jackie said she would send a text out and then see who responded to it. From that starting point, SAS, REST, and the tech volunteers (from Microsoft and other companies in Seattle) worked together to add more sophisticated features that would enhance its effectiveness. With the boost of Microsoft's volunteer support, they were able to move the text outreach to a more specialized and scalable platform.

160 "'The World's Terrible Truths are Never Solved by Turning a Blind Eye,' & Other Important Lessons Learned at Microsoft's 2016 //one-week Hackathon." *I Want Rest Blog*, October 17, 2016. Real Escape from the Sex Trade (September 28, 2019).

161 "We've Begun Our Year with a Real Game Changer." *REST News*, October 9, 2016. Real Escape from the Sex Trade (September 28, 2019).

The great thing about the text outreach, Jackie told me, is that it provides opportunities for people to know that places like REST exist. "We were immediately encouraged by the early results," the REST staff blogged after only a few months of using the platform. "Victims self-identified and were given individualized support to remove the barriers they faced."[162] So far, Jackie says she's reached out to over 6000 potential victims via text, sending out about 500 to 1000 messages at a time. The response rate is around sixteen percent, which—all things considered—is actually really high. That's hundreds more victims who might never have known about the services that are available to them. In 2017, for instance, forty women became clients at REST after receiving a text message from the system.[163] Jackie told me about some of these survivors:

- One woman who received a text from REST wasn't sure about it but responded anyway. Jackie then made time to meet with her in person. The woman wasn't ready to accept help right away, but Jackie continued to invest in that relationship, giving her time to see what REST had to offer. Eventually, the woman made the choice to let REST help her leave "the life" and get a place in a transition home.

---

162 Ibid.

163 Lee, Dave. "The chatbot taking on Seattle's sex trade." *BBC News*, November 25, 2017. BBC (September 28, 2019).

- Another client that REST contacted through text outreach already knew she wanted to get out of the sex trade but didn't know how. She had several children and was pregnant at the time; prostitution was the only way she could support her family, and she didn't feel like she had any other options. With REST's assistance, however, she was able to get a scholarship to learn a different trade.
- Another time, a REST advocate remembers, "I was on the hotline Sunday, and got a call from a woman in tears. She was assaulted and robbed the night before and needed help."[164] When the advocate wondered how the woman knew to contact REST, the woman replied, "You have texted me on all of my numbers and when this happened, I knew I could call you."[165] Thanks to the text outreach, she was aware that resources were available whenever she was ready for it. When she did call, the advocate was able to meet with her immediately and began giving her the support she needed.

Of course, there's a risk that comes with sending texts to potential victims. What if the perpetrator sees it? If a trafficker suspects that their victim is seeking a way out, the victim could end up in even more danger than she's in right now. Jackie told me that she gets asked all the time, "Aren't you scared?" To a certain extent, yes—that's why she is very

---

164 "Our Programs: Community Advocacy." *I Want Rest*, 2019. Real Escape from the Sex Trade (September 28, 2019).
165 Ibid.

intentional with the language that she uses in her texts. For example: "*My* name is Jackie…" or "*my* agency…" She does everything she can so that it doesn't look like the victim is the one initiating or pursuing the relationship. But she definitely doesn't let the risks keep her from reaching out. "It's better to get a resource out there than to be scared," she told me, because she's more afraid of the risks of *not* reaching out. Something is better than nothing.

And in some cases, incredible stories can unfold when a perpetrator sees a text message. Jackie told me about a time when she got a text response back, not from the victim but from the perpetrator who'd had her phone. Ashamed of his current way of life, which had caused him to lose custody of his child, he was looking for someone to help him turn over a new leaf. REST isn't equipped to offer services for traffickers, but Jackie still wanted to help him. "I believe in redemption," she told him. "What can I do to help you get involved in services?" They were able to connect him with case management workers to start the process of cleaning up his life and getting his child back. That's a remarkable example of the impact that a simple text can have—sometimes in unexpected ways.

This Victim Outreach platform is that it's an idea that can be utilized around the nation—in fact, law enforcement and victim service providers in other cities are already starting to incorporate this technology into their own work. Jackie, Liz, and the rest of Seattle Against Slavery's tech team also have no shortage of new ideas they'd love to implement, such as reaching out to victims through social media, not just text. There are so many possibilities to explore, which makes them hopeful for the future.

"We can dare to dream," says Jackie.

WATCHING OUT FOR EACH OTHER

On the other side of the world, another tech platform focuses on victim intervention by connecting Overseas Filipino Workers (OFWs) who are susceptible to labor trafficking. It's an app called OFW Watch, which incorporates social networking and geolocation technology so that OFWs can assist each other if someone finds themselves in an abusive or unsafe situation.

What's even more incredible is that the app was designed by a survivor herself: Myrna Padilla. Through her experience, she's found that one of the most effective strategies against modern-day slavery involves peers looking out for each other and responding to potential danger—and she's putting that strategy to work.

"The Philippines is a nation of migrant workers," she says. "At any given moment, there are over ten million of us working overseas as Overseas Filipino Workers (OFW) or expats. I know, because I spent twenty years working overseas to save my own two daughters from poverty" (OFW Watch 2016). In addition to being a huge source of overseas workers, who find jobs as domestic helpers, construction workers, technicians, etc., the Philippines is also known as a country with one of the highest percentages of Facebook users. According to Padilla, "Together, we account for over twenty million Facebook accounts."[166] Padilla leverages this tech-savviness among the Filipino people to spread usage of her app.

Born in an underdeveloped fishing village touching the Bohol Sea, Padilla grew up in dire poverty. She made ends meet by selling seaweed and singing at local festivals. "It was after one of these festivals that I was approached by a 'Recruiter' from Manila," she recalls, a woman who "told me the same story that a thousand young girls have been told…such beautiful lies."[167] The woman offered to help her save her family from poverty by singing in Japan. Padilla says, "I found myself believing in her with all my heart."[168]

Once she arrived in Manila, however, Padilla was told that before going to Japan, she had to pay off her debt, which included her transportation costs, recruitment fees, singing lessons, and food. "I kissed her hand softly and vowed to be the hardest worker she ever had," she said. "I would repay my debt. I was so deeply grateful and I was so naïve."[169] For the next year, she spent every bit of her time washing clothes by hand. "Twelve hours a day. Seven days a week. No day off.

---

166 "OFW Watch." Mynd Dynamic Team (September 28, 2019).
167 Ibid.
168 Ibid.
169 Ibid.

No pay."[170] Yet, she still believed that she was working toward a job that would rescue her family from poverty. It wasn't until Padilla's recruiter brought her to a singing "audition" in a nightclub that she realized the slavery she was being lured into. Before she could be sexually exploited, she slapped the man who approached her on stage and, remarkably, ran away.

Lost and despairing on the streets of Manila, Padilla wept for the loss of the deceptive dreams that had sustained her for so long. "For the first time in my life, I felt worthless."[171] But that darkest night would not crush her; hope arrived in the form of another domestic helper named Ponyang, who found her sobbing in a church and helped her get a job at a bakery. Padilla called Ponyang's noble intervention "my miracle."[172] From that day, she began to see the power of community, with fellow workers surrounding and supporting each other through small acts of kindness. In twenty years, she would be able to harness this power on a massive scale.

After a failed marriage left her with two daughters whom she loved fiercely, Padilla's goal was to get her daughters through college, for she knew that education paved the path out of poverty. In order to earn enough money, though, she had to find work overseas. For two decades, she worked as a domestic helper and nanny in Singapore, Taiwan, and Hong Kong. Her treatment varied by employer. "I have slept

---

170 Ibid.
171 Ibid.
172 Ibid.

on unheated kitchen floors in the dead of winter and eaten scraps fit only for a dog," she says. "But no abuse, verbal or otherwise, remotely compares to the pain and anguish of a mother separated from her children."[173] The heartache that she experienced while working abroad fueled her desire to (1) provide job opportunities in the Philippines so that families wouldn't have to separate, and (2) ensure safer and more dignified labor conditions for OFWs who did end up going overseas.

After working abroad for twelve years, Padilla glimpsed the thrill of technology for the first time, an encounter that would send her into a whirlwind of dreaming that she hadn't indulged since she was a little girl. It happened in Hong Kong, where she was charged with raising her Chinese boss's eight-year-old son. "Part of my responsibility was to make sure [Jonathan] did his homework and not play games," she explains.[174] At the time, "I didn't even have the slightest idea what a computer was."[175] As she looked over the young boy's shoulder, it captivated her. "Every time the little black thing was moved, there were changes in the screen," she remembers with a laugh.[176] Thanks to Jonathan, she learned "how to use

---

173 Ibid.
174 Ibid.
175 Sorsano, Freda Mae. "Former HK domestic worker develops app for OFWs." *Rappler*, October 25, 2014. Rappler (September 28, 2019).
176 Ibid.

a mouse, then Word applications, then surfing the Net, then e-mailing."[177]

From there, her enthusiasm grew.

After her daughters graduated college, she returned to Davao City in the Philippines and became a tech entrepreneur in 2006. She'd been inspired by the fact that people could perform services remotely via technology, such as maintaining websites or managing social media, a practice known as "outsourcing," so she tapped into this potential with her company Mynd Dynamic Team, Inc. It's a Business Process Outsourcing (BPO) company that creates information technology jobs for Filipinos. As Virtual Staff members, they're able to earn money while staying close to home. "We started with two people and an old computer offering bug testing and QA services to US clients," Padilla says.[178] Now, together with other BPO companies, Mynd Consulting has created jobs for "800,000 mothers, fathers, sons and daughters who will stay home in the Philippines, instead of being ripped from their families and shipped overseas."[179]

However, Padilla never forgot the men and women who spend years in someone else's home, far away from their families. She knew they were vulnerable to abuse, exploitation, and worse, and she wanted to do something to reduce the cases of labor trafficking among these OFWs. "There are

---

177 Ibid.
178 "OFW Watch." Mynd Dynamic Team (September 28, 2019).
179 Ibid.

ten million of us working all over the world. No government agency can effectively watch over such overwhelming numbers," she says. "However, social media thrives on overwhelming numbers. We must use this fact to watch out for each other."[180] She'd already seen that OFWs tried to do what they could to help out fellow Filipinos if they were in trouble, just like her interaction with Ponyang on the streets of Manila. Through the OFW Watch app, Padilla made it possible for these lifesaving connections to happen on thousands of phones all over the world.

Funded by the profits from Mynd Dynamic Team, the company spun out OFW Watch as a community service initiative to support unity among OFWs. Migrant workers with the app strengthen their contact with the outside world, which makes it more difficult for employers to abuse them without repercussions. And for Filipinos who are already familiar with social media platforms like Facebook, it's easy for them to get started. "All they have to do is download the application and register [with their Facebook account]. Once a person becomes a member of OFW Watch, they will automatically be included in the database," Padilla explains.[181] Even OFWs who are in safe and successful situations—*especially* these OFWs—are urged to register, to help out those who may be less fortunate.

---

180 Ibid.
181 Sorsano, Freda Mae. "Former HK domestic worker develops app for OFWs." *Rappler*, October 25, 2014. Rappler (September 28, 2019).

The app, which is available in both mobile and web versions, detects the user's location to connect him/her to "other Filipinos in your area who share the same dialect, hometown, and profession."[182] It includes a "Work Journal" where they can record their working conditions, the ability to report cases of suspected abuse or missing workers, and an "SOS" button if they need to send a request for immediate help. All communication is encrypted for security. Most importantly, the app will privately alert users if an OFW near them is in a crisis. Then, they'll be able to contact local authorities or take other suggested courses of action.

It's spreading like wildfire.

Even without advertising campaigns—simply by word of mouth—OFW Watch had over 100,000 members as of October 2014. And this was only the beginning. Padilla explains it with a touch of Filipino pride: "It's the nature of Filipinos to volunteer."[183] A few years later, Mynd Dynamic Team, Inc. partnered with the Philippines Department of Labor and Employment (DoLE) and the Overseas Workers Welfare Administration to unroll the app in targeted locations. "We are eyeing to reach countries where our OFWs are," she shared, describing their plan to spread usage of the app to the Middle East and beyond.[184] They launched a pilot

---

182 "OFW Watch." Mynd Dynamic Team (September 28, 2019).

183 Sorsano, Freda Mae. "Former HK domestic worker develops app for OFWs." *Rappler*, October 25, 2014. Rappler (September 28, 2019).

184 Padillo, Maya. "OFW Watch app ready for download." *Business World*, February 5, 2018. Business World Publishing (September 28,

project in Hong Kong in February 2017—it's fitting that they chose the city where Padilla first encountered technology as an OFW herself.

Of course, she credits the app's success to the Filipino people themselves. "The concept behind OFW Watch is simple… we are NOT helpless," she writes on the app's website. "We are successful, strong and technically savvy."[185] The app may allow for more effective communication and more immediate assistance, but a desire to uphold the dignity of their fellow Filipinos is already woven into their identity.

As for herself?

"As a young girl, I was the victim of human trafficking," she says.[186] Today, Padilla calls herself "a woman, now empowered with technology, [who] is compelled to fight on behalf of the sisters she has left behind."[187]

**

Although not all victims have access to a cellular device, it's a powerful means of outreach for those who do. Whether it's allowing victims to text a national helpline, sending mass text messages to potential domestic sex trafficking victims, or enabling overseas foreign workers to respond if a fellow

_____

2019).

185 "OFW Watch." Mynd Dynamic Team (September 28, 2019).

186 Ibid.

187 Ibid.

OFW is in danger of becoming a labor trafficking victim, technology provides a diversity of opportunities to connect with victims directly.

Oftentimes, victims feel like no one sees their plight, that they don't have anyone to go to for help. When they get a ping on their phone, and they know that there's a heartbeat on the other side, someone who cares about their well-being and will do what they can to get them out of that situation, it can nudge them to finally take the chance to seize freedom for themselves.

It's a beacon of hope.

CHAPTER 7:

EMPOWER SURVIVORS

"Because of the empowering nature of technology, I started dreaming..."

—MYRNA PADILLA, LABOR TRAFFICKING SURVIVOR AND FOUNDER OF MYND DYNAMIC TEAM, INC.[188]

Life after leaving a trafficking situation is an uphill battle. "They took away my innocence and the hope of being a self-assured person," says Guadalupe Pérez Castillo, three years after escaping the woman who had forced her into domestic servitude at age ten.[189] After nearly three decades

---

188 "OFW Watch." Mynd Dynamic Team (September 28, 2019).
189 Romo, Rafael. "Thirty years living and working as a modern-day slave." *The CNN Freedom Project*, April 28, 2017. CNN (September 28, 2019).

of sexual and physical abuse in the most degrading conditions, Pérez "couldn't stop" falling back into an entrapped way of life.[190] She had to fight the impulse to do the dishes and make the beds whenever she entered a house or hotel. Even simple decisions, such as claiming a favorite ice cream flavor, were excruciating for someone who had been trained to suppress her opinion for so long.

This decision-making is an element that REST, a Victim Service Provider (VSP) organization in Seattle, recognizes as key in establishing independence from an exploiter. At REST's drop-in center for those seeking respite from the sex trade before deciding to leave "the life" for good, they've placed a little coffee station right in front, where clients can select a hot beverage when they first arrive. "Coffee or tea?" It's a simple question, but for survivors, it's a revolutionary shift in perspective—they have the power to *choose* for themselves. And it helps them ever so slightly understand that their voice matters.

"That healing process won't begin until you can get away from your exploiter," says Catie Hart, who had met her boyfriend-turned-trafficker outside a night club in 1998, when she was an "insecure" eighteen-year-old who had just moved to San Francisco for college.[191] Before long, he had coerced her into sex work at local strip clubs, a slavery that lasted for

---

190 Ibid.
191 Jennings, Cheryl. "Beyond the Headlines: Human Trafficking." *ABC 7 News*, December 16, 2014. ABC, Inc. (September 28, 2019).

seven years. "It got to the point where I was working ninety-eight hours a week…and when I wasn't at work he would sleep-deprive me in order to keep me under his control," Hart remembered.[192] He threatened to kill her if she tried to leave, blackmailing her with the secrets she'd once told him as his girlfriend. It took every ounce of strength she could muster to finally pack all her belongings in a garbage bag and run away.

Now, Hart is an accomplished professional with a degree in sociology; she collaborates with the San Francisco Police Department, offers support to other survivors, and trains thousands of social workers, probation officers, and county council members about the issue.[193] But it wasn't an easy road out. "You can oftentimes feel like you've betrayed yourself," she says; that internal shame, combined with the stigma that society often places around them, can be enough to keep anyone from pursuing new opportunities.[194]

For a young woman named Nadège, this stifling shame is all too true. "My past already destroyed my future," she said during an interview with CNN, her voice trembling.[195] A Nigerian survivor who fled after nearly a year in a Parisian prostitution network, she's seen that "there are brains

---

192 Ibid.
193 "About Catie." *Catie Hart*, 2017. Catie Hart (September 28, 2019).
194 Jennings, Cheryl. "Beyond the Headlines: Human Trafficking." *ABC 7 News*, December 16, 2014. ABC, Inc. (September 28, 2019).
195 Andrews, Frank. "The Paris park where Nigerian women and forced into prostitution." *The CNN Freedom Project*, October 5, 2018. CNN (September 28, 2019).

and talent wasting" among the tens of thousands of sex trafficking victims like herself, who appear on the streets of French parks at dusk.[196] However, now that she's free, Nadège believes it's too late to recover the capabilities that she lost. "No matter what I am tomorrow, I'm still going to be useless," she said, "because I can't proudly say my story. I can't proudly tell the world who I am."[197]

Add that to the sheer difficulty of learning the skills to secure a well-paying job, and survivors find themselves hard-put to overcome the vulnerability that led to exploitation in the first place. Without the proper legal support, trauma counseling, and skills training, many survivors remain prone to being re-trafficked—pulled back toward the traffickers who entice or ensnare them into their control until they cannot even conceive of what freedom would be like. It's not uncommon for them to slip in and out of shelters multiple times, in a brutally hopeless cycle. "But there *is* a better life out there," Hart insists.[198]

Here's an area where technology's waiting with huge potential.

In recent years, more and more survivors are taking technology into their own hands as a means to move beyond their past. Learning how to use products like Microsoft

---

196 Ibid.
197 Ibid.
198 Jennings, Cheryl. "Beyond the Headlines: Human Trafficking." *ABC 7 News*, December 16, 2014. ABC, Inc. (September 28, 2019).

Word and Excel gives survivors a competitive edge in the job market, while learning web development and computer programming opens up fantastic opportunities to enter the tech industry itself. Many survivors are also designing technology to combat human trafficking, leveraging their own experience and passion for a deeply personal cause. This is one of the most exciting areas I've encountered in the intersection of technology and anti-trafficking work—a way for survivors to find purpose and power, equipped to explore a future that will benefit us all.

ONE STARFISH AT A TIME

I don't remember exactly when I discovered the tight-knit social enterprise called Starfish Project; I simply stumbled across their page on Instagram and instantly fell in love with their mission. Among other qualities, I admire the way that they empower sex trafficking survivors through computer training.

With a team in the United States coordinating operations in several undisclosed locations in Southeast Asia, founder Jenny McGee lives in Thailand with her husband and three children, where she spends her days befriending the young girls and women who work in the neighborhood brothels. She certainly lives up to her company's name, which is reminiscent of a well-known story: a man tosses stranded sea stars back into the ocean, unfazed by the thousands upon thousands lying on the shore. There's no way he could save them all, yet he stoops deliberately, intent on making a difference to each one he's able to touch.

That's what Starfish Project does: restoring hope to sexually exploited women, one life at a time.

It started in 2006, when Jenny—who had already lived in Asia for four years and was fluent in the local language—volunteered to translate for a friend who wanted to reach out to brothel workers. Before then, Jenny hadn't given much thought to the women she passed on the street. "When I started hearing their stories, I was really shocked," she remembers.[199] These women had traveled thirty to forty hours by train to get to the city, leaving the countryside villages that were all they'd ever known. Some of them were as young as twelve or thirteen. "They'd come from homes with no running water, dirt floors, and most of the time they hadn't had any education," Jenny says.[200] They didn't know how to read or write, and familiarity with technology was out of the question.

"A lot of the women are really being tricked into working in the brothels. They don't know what they're getting into when they arrive there," Jenny explains, adding that they're often deceived by a trusted relative, such as a sister or an uncle.[201] Once in the brothels, they are threatened and beaten into submission. One survivor remembers, "The

---

199 "Episode 5—From Trafficked to Transformed: Jenny McGee of the Starfish Project." *Jessica Honegger*, February 28, 2018. Jessica Honegger (September 28, 2019).
200 Ibid.
201 Ibid.

owner told me that I had to work for him or he would kill me."[202] Another explained that her uncle sold her to a brothel owner who fabricated a debt to keep her in bondage. "I was told I owed the boss two months' wages and had to sign a contract to work for him for two years," she said. "After the contract was up, he said I still owed more money. With no other means to pay off the debt, I felt trapped."[203] With no education, skills, or support, and betrayed by the people they thought they could trust, it's no wonder that these young girls remain helpless.

"The girls live in the shops, which are dark and have no windows," Jenny says.[204] The brothels take many forms, operating within massage parlors or karaoke bars or even a closet-like space that fits only one girl. In these squalid conditions, the girls are expected to work seven days a week, seeing ten to twelve customers on a "good" day. It's devastating to imagine that this is their "normal." In March 2019, Jenny blogged about one girl she met sitting in front of a glass window, noticing that "she was clearly the bait to lure the customers into the brothel. She wore the make-up of a forty-year-old, but she had the face of a child."[205] Jenny had seen

---

202 Culp, Alice. "Starfish Project offers hope and redemption to exploited women." *South Bend Tribune*, July 24, 2016. GateHouse Media (September 28, 2019).

203 Ibid.

204 Ibid.

205 McGee, Jenny. "Behind the Scenes: 12 years old." Starfish Project, March 19, 2019. Starfish Project (September 28, 2018).

many girls like this one throughout her years in Asia, but it still hit her as if it were her first time coming face-to-face with this heart-wrenching injustice: the tears, the fury, the desire to take this twelve-year-old child by the hand and tell her that someone cares about her.

"I can't get her face out of my mind, and I weep for her," Jenny wrote. "I am struck at how different [my twelve-year-old son's] life is from this girl, who in another life, might be his classmate and sit next to him in school."[206] Like so many, this girl had been told all her life that she was not needed. That she was not useful. That she was worthless.

Jenny embarked on a mission to overturn that lie.

As she became familiar with the women and girls in these brothels, she realized that "they were really there for economic reasons."[207] Too often, the girls seem to "choose" to stay in the brothels because they don't have any other options. For instance, their illiteracy limited their career choices—even waitressing wasn't an option because they couldn't write down orders. Sometimes their parents had abandoned them, leaving the girls desperate for any way to feed themselves; the brothel seemed like the only viable lifestyle. "In order to survive, I was forced to sell my body and my self-respect," one

---

206 Ibid.

207 "Episode 5—From Trafficked to Transformed: Jenny McGee of the Starfish Project." *Jessica Honegger*, February 28, 2018. Jessica Honegger (September 28, 2019).

survivor remembers.[208] And they eventually move up in the system, like Zi Yun, a woman who had begun managing her own brothel, "recruiting other girls into that same darkness" even though she knew "it was a terrible lifestyle."[209] In order to break that cycle, Jenny needed to find a way to equip these women with better job opportunities. "We needed economic solutions," she said.[210]

To fill that need, she created Starfish Project.

The enterprise officially launched in 2006, with Jenny leveraging technology's power to facilitate collaboration that spans continents: her team in Asia holds birthday parties and initiates conversations with the women who have never received these basic kindnesses; donors and customers lend their support while a "retired librarian in Arizona writes thank you notes," and a very committed "instafamily" community follows along on Instagram.[211] At first glance, Starfish Project is a fashion company, selling jewelry handmade by survivors of sex trafficking. But behind the scenes, they do much more—equipping these women to step into the

208 Culp, Alice. "Starfish Project offers hope and redemption to exploited women." *South Bend Tribune*, July 24, 2016. GateHouse Media (September 28, 2019).

209 "Zi Yun: A Story of Hope." *YouTube*, December 30, 2016. Starfish Project (September 28, 2019).

210 "Episode 5—From Trafficked to Transformed: Jenny McGee of the Starfish Project." *Jessica Honegger*, February 28, 2018. Jessica Honegger (September 28, 2019).

211 "Meet Virginia Hawkins, Chief Strategy Officer at Starfish Project." *Starfish Project*, October 24, 2017. Starfish Project (September 28, 2019).

professional world, helping them find a career that they're passionate about, and creating a community where they can belong.

As part of their outreach model, Jenny and her co-workers—many of whom, including Zi Yun, are survivors themselves—never pressure anyone to join the Starfish family. They're careful to cultivate friendships and offer them an alternative, letting them decide on their own time. Trust is a huge issue, because "they were tricked by their own family members to end up in this brothel," so it takes a lot of time and intention to build a relationship to the point where they would be willing to trust a white woman from the United States.[212] In fact, one girl in the Starfish Project family told Jenny that, "The day I met you...I kind of thought you were going to traffic me again, but I had nowhere else to go, so I just decided to come with you."[213] Thankfully, her desperation paved the path to her healing.

And it's just as transformative for the women on the other side: Zi Yun reflects, "I used to go to these girls every day, to look for them, to recruit them—'Go and work at the karaoke bars...You can make lots of money!'"[214] She'd carried on the lies that had lured her into prostitution in the first place.

---

212 "Episode 5—From Trafficked to Transformed: Jenny McGee of the Starfish Project." *Jessica Honegger*, February 28, 2018. Jessica Honegger (September 28, 2019).

213 Ibid.

214 "Zi Yun: A Story of Hope." *YouTube*, December 30, 2016. Starfish Project (September 28, 2019).

"But today," she says, "I go back to those places to bring these sweet girls and women out of there to work at Starfish Project."[215] Her life has completely turned around.

Once a woman becomes a member of Starfish Project, she enters a Holistic Care Program where she receives safe housing, counseling programs, medical evaluations, and educational assessments in order to develop an "individualized growth plan…based on her education levels, her needs, and how she's doing emotionally."[216] She is not just another data entry in a table; she's an individual with her own story and her own hopes for the future. Jenny doesn't take this lightly.

Truly, it's a personalized starfish approach.

After learning how to read and write in their local language, the women are eligible for computer training—the next level of literacy in modern society. "All of our girls get certified in Microsoft programs—that's huge for them," says Jenny.[217] The fact that they're offered the computer training is incredible for these girls; it's like saying "I believe in you," when no one ever has before. Many of them had only reached second grade before coming to Starfish Project, so learning technology had never even been on their radar.

Jenny encourages each of these women to participate in this training, no matter which career they're intending

---

215 Ibid.

216 "Episode 5—From Trafficked to Transformed: Jenny McGee of the Starfish Project." *Jessica Honegger*, February 28, 2018. Jessica Honegger (September 28, 2019).

217 Ibid.

to pursue. Given the prevalence of digital media today, she knows that it will not only give them marketable skills but also a boost to their confidence when they realize how much they are capable of. When they master Microsoft Word, Excel, and (for some of them) Outlook, it's a tremendous milestone. "They'll cry. We have a big graduation ceremony when they get their certificates," Jenny says.[218] Proficiency with these Microsoft programs helps define the difference between vulnerability and independence.

With this advantage entering the professional world, the women are empowered to pursue career paths that personally excite them. Jenny explains, "Once they've gone through those computer training programs, we'll help sponsor them to study outside of Starfish."[219] While the end product of Starfish's business is hand-crafted jewelry, the girls have the opportunity to explore applicable skills throughout the production process, from marketing to graphic design to photography to accounting. It's not just about the jewelry. Rather, it's a launching pad to learn tools that they will use in future careers.

Most women stay with Starfish Project for around three to four years. "Our goal isn't really to have them work at Starfish forever," Jenny says. "We really want to train them up, see them come to a healthy, stable place, and then have real skills

---

218 Ibid.
219 Ibid.

that they can take to the outside world."[220] Some of them do continue with the company in various roles, however. For instance, Lay Lay was promoted to Finished Products Inventory Manager, using her Microsoft Word and Excel skills in her daily work as she also works toward the Microsoft Outlook certification.[221] And there's Fay, who had doubted that she would survive much longer in the brothels when a Starfish Project outreach team offered her a way out. Now, after studying "really hard" to complete her computer training and accounting programs, she works as Starfish's accounting assistant and is studying for a bachelor's degree.[222]

For each of these women, it's surreal to be able to identify their personal dreams and slowly work toward them. "It meant a lot to have the Starfish staff recognize my potential," Fay says.[223] Although their past is stacked against them, the support from Starfish helps them overcome the stigma and insecurities they face during their journey to acquire dignified work.

And it's crazy that they have technology at their fingertips whereas, in their previous lives, they were simply trying to survive each day. Chang Chang, the Raw Material Inventory Manager, explains that "I use the computer and

220 Ibid.
221 "Educate Her: Lay Lay." *Starfish Project*, October 30, 2018. Starfish Project (September 28, 2019).
222 "Fay: My Story of Hope." *Starfish Project*, 2019. Starfish Project (September 28, 2019).
223 Ibid.

inventory management software to check our inventory level and make sure the production process goes smoothly."[224] She never takes her everyday tasks for granted. "Before arriving, I had never used a computer," she remembers. "Now, I use a computer every day for work and I am a certified Microsoft Expert. I have so many opportunities to learn here."[225] She's had the chance to gain independence and confidence, finding a brand new life with her Starfish family.

Through Starfish Project's online #educateHer campaign, donors can become part of each woman's story by contributing toward the cost of a computer for them, so that they can continue their studies. That makes the technology training extra special for these survivors—it isn't just about learning the software programs themselves, it's knowing that they are surrounded by an incredible community who are rooting for them every step of the way.

SHOOTING FOR THE STARS

What if survivors discovered they could not only master existing technology but become software programmers themselves? With its holistic model, AnnieCannons is doing just that—inspiring survivors to tap into their abilities in the technology industry. It's a remarkable way to empower their

---

224 "Chang Chang: My Story of Hope." *Starfish Project*, 2019. Starfish Project (September 28, 2019).

225 Ibid.

new life of freedom as well as to enable survivor-designed tech initiatives to combat human trafficking.

In Silicon Valley back in September 2013, Jessica Hubley worked as an attorney by day and author by night, writing a nonfiction book about the global human trafficking crisis and the ways that technology could be leveraged to help. At the same time, researcher Laura Hackney—who'd previously served on the Human Trafficking Task Force in the San Francisco Police Department—was planning a flight to Southeast Asia as part of Stanford University's Anti-Trafficking Project. Jessica had gotten connected with Laura while working on her book, and she remembers when Laura "asked if I wanted to come along" to interview women who had been trafficked as brides between China and Myanmar.[226]

In the Mekong Sub-Region of Myanmar, the two Stanford alumni "met and interviewed nine people who were victims of human trafficking and they all said the same thing."[227] In the majority of stories, she could trace common themes between the women in Asia and the women in America: They were living in poverty. They were desperate for work. They trusted someone who offered them an opportunity. But that opportunity turned out to be a hoax, and they found themselves in the trafficker's control, sexually exploited with seemingly no way out.

---

226 "Causes: AnnieCannons." *Charity Matters*, November 16, 2017. Charity Matters (September 28, 2019).

227 Ibid.

Far too often, anti-trafficking work is equated with "rescuing victims" via dramatic raids on hotels or brothels. However, without the proper resources and support, survivors are likely to slip in and out of shelters or back into the life from which they were removed. Not only have they been psychologically cramped by their captors to a powerful level of dependency or terror, but even if they wanted to pursue dignified work, the job search is stacked against them. Their record of sex work, drug use, or associated criminal activity often deters companies from hiring them, so they revert back to the only life they know. For example, Catie Hart continued to work in a strip club for two years after escaping from her boyfriend-turned-exploiter, just to make ends meet while she pursued her university degree. "I didn't feel like I had other options," she said.[228]

Laura voiced her frustration at the status quo: "I was hearing over and over again [that] now we can rescue people and then they'll be free.'"[229] But she knew that even after a rescue operation, these women still weren't free. They received excellent "legal aid, counseling, and intensive case management" services, but there was something missing: survivors

---

228 Nazaryan, Arthur. "This sex trafficking survivor is moving on—by learning how to code." *PRI GlobalPost*, August 17, 2018. Public Radio International (September 28, 2019).

229 Aguilera, Diana. "Human Rights at Home: How two alums are confronting slavery in their backyard." *Stanford Magazine*, September 6, 2017. Medium (September 28, 2018).

still weren't able to recover an independent life.[230] "It kept me up at night," she said (Aguilera 2017). There had to be a way to dismantle their vulnerability in order to keep survivors permanently free from their traffickers.

Jessica felt the same way. She and Laura were convinced that lack of economic opportunity for these women was the underlying problem. If they were trained in valuable job skills, they would be less vulnerable to traffickers who take advantage of their financial desperation. Unfortunately, the anti-trafficking community had "entirely discounted survivors' value as intelligent human resources capable of great economic productivity."[231] Many shelters for trafficking survivors did offer skill-training classes such as jewelry or pottery making, but according to Jessica, these were not "skills that a person could use to reasonably make a living, much less allow him or her to become economically or politically empowered."[232] They needed skills that would equip them to find higher-income jobs offering stability and independence.

What about training in the tech field? Upon returning to the United States, Jessica recalls that suddenly, "I was seeing

---

230 Connel, Joanie. "Turning Tragedy into REAL Life: Empowering Survivors of Human Trafficking." Women Lead Radio, August 21, 2017. Connected Women of Influence (September 28, 2019).

231 Beer, Kieran. "Giving Victims of Sex Trafficking Their Due." *ACAMS Today*, March 28, 2019. Association of Certified Anti-Money Laundering Specialists (September 28, 2019).

232 Hepburn, Stephanie. "AnnieCannons is Helping Human Trafficking Survivors Become Tech Experts." *Huffington Post*, October 19, 2017. Verizon Media (September 28, 2019).

so many people in software development making $400 an hour writing code and couldn't help but wonder what if we taught these women victims of human trafficking how to do this?"[233]

It was a eureka moment for Laura and Jessica. "We have this huge pool of untapped talent in this very profitable skill, and we have all of this demand for this very profitable skill... why not put them together?"[234]

So that's what they did. They researched the ins and outs of running a nonprofit, established relationships with nearby victim service provider organizations, and assembled a curriculum to introduce the technical know-how that someone would need to get started in the tech world. And in the fall of 2015, they held their first classes at the Alameda County Family Justice Center in Oakland, California.

**

Their non-profit organization, called AnnieCannons, operates with a three-pronged approach:

First, **training**. Through a coding boot camp, Jessica and Laura—joined by a team of volunteer developers and designers—unroll a curriculum consisting of six-month

233 "Causes: AnnieCannons." *Charity Matters*, November 16, 2017. Charity Matters (September 28, 2019).

234 Nazaryan, Arthur. "This sex trafficking survivor is moving on—by learning how to code." *PRI GlobalPost*, August 17, 2018. Public Radio International (September 28, 2019).

courses, four hours per day, four days a week. The courses cover basic digital literacy and the software life cycle, as well as HTML, CSS, and JavaScript for front-end web design.[235] Basically, their goal is to equip their students with an impressive amount of skills within a short timeline, so they can start supporting themselves through web development work as soon as possible.

It's an intensive model, but it's designed with survivor-specific needs in mind. And it's quite a diverse group to accommodate, consisting of students who have been referred to AnnieCannons from shelters, aid centers, and case managers in the Bay Area who've "seen their potential despite the obstacles life has thrown their way."[236] While the majority of their students are U.S. citizens local to Northern California, Jessica adds that they "range from having been born into slavery, [with] no memory of not being in their trafficking situation before they got away, all the way up to having a... college or graduate degree prior to having a romantic partner exploit them."[237]

One of these was Catie Hart. As a sex trafficking survivor, Catie had been working as a consultant to law enforcement and social service agencies, leveraging her experiences to

---

235 Ibid.
236 "Pitching Their Stories: AnnieCannons." *YouTube*, November 9, 2017. Solve—MIT (September 28, 2019).
237 Nazaryan, Arthur. "This sex trafficking survivor is moving on—by learning how to code." *PRI GlobalPost*, August 17, 2018. Public Radio International (September 28, 2019).

advise on best practices for supporting victims and survivors of trafficking. Jessica and Laura connected with her at first because of Catie's consulting work... but when Catie learned about AnnieCannons' program, she decided to enroll in the training herself.

From cohort to cohort, Jessica and Laura have worked with women (and one man), U.S. citizens and foreign nationals, labor and sex trafficking survivors. What do these students all have in common? According to Jessica, "They're all natural problem-solvers, and a vastly undervalued human talent."[238] She and Laura do all they can to support them in making the most of their innate abilities, despite the obstacles that may impede their way.

For many AnnieCannons students, consistent attendance is a major hurdle. For example, Hart said that while her cohort originally began with eight students, "realistically only three of us are really gonna make it through."[239] To counteract these hindrances, AnnieCannons schedules their "boot camp" modules so that students can still attend while working another job. The organization also provides in-house childcare during class sessions for mothers who would otherwise not be able to attend. Sometimes, children even hang out in the classrooms. That's how it was for Claire

---

238 "Pitching Their Stories: AnnieCannons." *YouTube*, November 9, 2017. Solve—MIT (September 28, 2019).

239 Nazaryan, Arthur. "This sex trafficking survivor is moving on—by learning how to code." *PRI GlobalPost*, August 17, 2018. Public Radio International (September 28, 2019).

(pseudonym), who spent time with AnnieCannons as both a student and a teaching assistant. Her son often sat in on the classes when she was working, and AnnieCannons blogged that they were "excited to see him learn much more about software programming from his mom over the coming years."[240]

This level of comfort in the classroom is something that's strongly emphasized at AnnieCannons. "There are certain parts of the class that are inherently therapeutic," Jessica says.[241] She and Laura model a nonjudgmental, supportive environment where they open the floor at the beginning of each class, if anyone wants to talk about what's happening in their lives. Laura adds, "We make sure that they have a way to reach out and check in with us on a regular basis."[242] Whether it's an open-table discussion or a water-cooler banter, the two of them make conversations as organic as possible.

However, they don't pressure anyone to talk about their experiences of exploitation. Rather, they encourage their students to only share what they're comfortable, when they're ready. "We say, early and often, that no one is obligated to share anything with us about their past," Jessica emphasizes.

240 "Seattle Against Slavery's Web Platform to Fight Demand." *Annie-Cannons Blog*, December 19, 2018. AnnieCannons (September 28, 2019).

241 Connel, Joanie. "Turning Tragedy into REAL Life: Empowering Survivors of Human Trafficking." Women Lead Radio, August 21, 2017. Connected Women of Influence (September 28, 2019).

242 Ibid.

Everyone opens up in their own time, in different ways. "Some people have a day where something opens the floodgates and they share very broadly for a week, some people will always keep quiet, and we think that's their decision to make."[243] Whatever it takes to move beyond their trauma, *that's* the focus: transforming trafficking survivors into technology professionals.

"We are constantly reminding students not to apologize for not knowing something," Jessica says, "not to apologize for who they are or where they've come from. We are constantly trying to build up their confidence, not just with the larger products but even in daily algorithm exercises."[244] Especially since the average trafficking survivor in the United States left school around age twelve, the interactive exercises and positive reinforcement help them celebrate small successes throughout the class (SFHTML5 2016). "You know, letting them see like *oh! I got that right*," Jessica explains.[245]

Really, it's not about human trafficking; it's not about survivors or victims or trauma or shame. It's about seizing the future that otherwise would have been stolen away from them. Laura and Jessica chose to reflect this priority in the namesake of their enterprise: a female astronomer who, in her day, made breakthrough discoveries in measuring and classifying stars. "We think [Annie Jump Cannon]

---

243 Ibid.
244 Ibid.
245 Ibid.

represents the innovative power of the underappreciated," Laura explains.[246] That's exactly how she and Jessica define their mission: they're determined to overturn the limited career options that female trafficking survivors face. It's primarily about "women supporting each other," says Jessica. "We didn't want to name it about freedom or slavery; that's all about the past. We want it to be about the future of what they can become."[247]

It's small shifts in perspective like these that lead to breathtaking transformation.

**

Beyond technical training, the second prong of Annie-Cannons' program is **income**: enabling their students to find freelance tech work so they can begin supporting themselves almost immediately.

For many survivors, learning the technical skills necessary to become a software professional—challenging as that may be—is a paltry barrier compared to the intangible roadblocks that hamper their entrance into the tech world. The factors could be external (employers tend to avoid candidates with questionable police records, etc.) or internal ("imposter

---

246 Hubley, Jessica. "Why the name 'AnnieCannons'?." *YouTube*, November 25, 2018. AnnieCannons (September 28, 2019).

247 Aguilera, Diana. "Human Rights at Home: How two alums are confronting slavery in their backyard." *Stanford Magazine*, September 6, 2017. Medium (September 28, 2018).

syndrome" is strong for women who grew up poor, with little education, and had been told over and over again that they are worthless), but either way, if the women had to navigate the industry on their own, they'd be swimming upstream.

That's why AnnieCannons also functions as a job agency for its students. Jessica and Laura wanted to offer these women an "economically viable alternative [to sex work], without the judgment sex workers often get from prospective employers."[248] To streamline the daunting job search process, therefore, AnnieCannons handles all the logistics of accounting, contracting, and managing clients on behalf of the students. "The only thing they have to do to make money is be good at software engineering," Jessica says.[249] That's really all they should be concerned about—getting hands-on experience in the tech industry that will catapult them toward future job opportunities.

In fact, a unique piece of AnnieCannons' model is that the students don't have to wait until they've completed their training before they can begin building actual products. Instead, they can directly monetize their skills while building their portfolio. With AnnieCannons matching students to projects, the women can work as subcontractors for a variety of third-party clients, "including small businesses that need

248 Nazaryan, Arthur. "This sex trafficking survivor is moving on—by learning how to code." *PRI GlobalPost*, August 17, 2018. Public Radio International (September 28, 2019).

249 Ibid.

web development, private foundations paying for complex software platforms, and well-known technology companies outsourcing data entry."[250] As they learn on the job, they improve their skills, add to their repertoire, and earn a stable wage that in turn makes it easier for them to consistently attend class. Eventually, they'll be highly qualified to take on a competitive career.

For Catie Hart, this part of the AnnieCannons program was life-changing. Even as a survivor, she had been compelled to continue working in strip clubs just to get herself through college, because she didn't have any other economically viable alternatives. Now, AnnieCannons helped her find "actual real financial security."[251] Having completed the first phase of coursework, she was matched with a client and then took on database management and cleanup work for $20 per hour. "I've never been happier…having a steady paycheck for the first time since I was like sixteen," she remarked. "I know I'm going to get paid every two weeks," she said, "and I can start to…settle into my life, finally."[252] She also appreciates that the work is not directly linked to her past life, as her police department consulting had been. "I'm so excited for

---

250 Hepburn, Stephanie. "AnnieCannons is Helping Human Trafficking Survivors Become Tech Experts." *Huffington Post,* October 19, 2017. Verizon Media (September 28, 2019).

251 Nazaryan, Arthur. "This sex trafficking survivor is moving on—by learning how to code." *PRI GlobalPost,* August 17, 2018. Public Radio International (September 28, 2019).

252 Ibid.

the future for the first time in twenty years," she said.[253] It's about moving forward, not dwelling in the past.

Claire, a mother of two boys who took classes while working nights as a security officer and then, after "rocking our training," became a teaching assistant (and, after graduation, a fully certified instructor) for AnnieCannons, also found tremendous growth by taking on jobs outside of her coursework.[254] She tackled one of her major projects in 2018, when the grassroots NGO Seattle Against Slavery approached AnnieCannons for help. They were looking for a web development partner who could help create a website to promote their Freedom Signal platform, and Claire eagerly undertook the task. She had been practicing her skills with WordPress sites, so creating the Freedom Signal website was a perfect "next step in her web development career."[255]

Working hard to implement "a more complex display and functionality" than anything she'd built previously, Claire had the official Freedom Signal website ready for launch in November 2018.[256] It's an incredible testament to how much she's grown since the day she was referred to AnnieCannons by the Alameda County Family Justice Center a few years before. Once trapped in an exploitative situation, now

253 Ibid.
254 "Seattle Against Slavery's Web Platform to Fight Demand." *Annie-Cannons Blog*, December 19, 2018. AnnieCannons (September 28, 2019).
255 Ibid.
256 Ibid.

she's helping an anti-trafficking organization expand their own technology that's combating human trafficking all over the country.

** **

The last piece of AnnieCannons' model is creating **student-ideated technology**. They unroll their training through the lens of trauma-informed technology, which means that each student is encouraged to develop software solutions to problems that she personally cares about. "We ask the students very early in the class, 'What's a problem that you've seen in your life or community that you think led to your exploitation?'" Jessica explains. "And then we use those problems as anchors to discuss how software might be developed to solve a piece of that problem."[257]

Often, the women choose to focus on projects that fight the underlying causes of human trafficking. There's definitely no shortage of these causes! The reality is that "human trafficking is a manifestation of a lot of other social problems," Jessica explains.[258] "We see large-scale social issues like poverty, discrimination, and violence create the vulnerabilities

---

257 Connel, Joanie. "Turning Tragedy into REAL Life: Empowering Survivors of Human Trafficking." Women Lead Radio, August 21, 2017. Connected Women of Influence (September 28, 2019).
258 Ibid.

that drive a cycle of exploitation."[259] In order to eradicate human trafficking, we must get at these gnarly roots.

With AnnieCannons' product-based learning model, Jessica is a firm believer that "survivors with technology opportunities are actually the best people to help society break that cycle [of exploitation]."[260] Because they've been there. They've grown up in broken homes, where money is scarce and parents are absent and school is a low priority. They've experienced neglect and abuse in the foster care system. They know what it's like to live in constant fear of violence from people they should have been able to trust, and they are all too familiar with society's averted eyes, which make them feel ignored, invisible, or—even worse—that they are to blame for "letting themselves" be taken into a trafficker's control.

As one example of a trauma-informed project, AnnieCannons' inaugural class of 2015 worked together to build Survivors.io, a website that addresses the dearth of data on sexual assaults. The site applies crowdsourcing methods to counteract the chronic lack of reporting around sexual assaults. Anyone can submit an anonymous sexual assault report on the site, which then synthesizes the data to gain a better understanding of victims' demographics.

Another AnnieCannons student recognized that the U.S. court system often obstructs a victim from obtaining

---

259 "Pitching Their Stories: AnnieCannons." *YouTube*, November 9, 2017. Solve—MIT (September 28, 2019).

260 Ibid.

protection against a trafficker. To facilitate the process, she designed an app to make it easier to get a legal restraining order.

With all of these projects, Jessica and Laura work with the students to discuss realistic goals: how to build the software most effectively, how it would be expanded over time, and how it might actually be launched into the market. Laura says that one of the most exciting things she gets to see is "when students start working on their own projects to address issues or problems that they've seen in their own lives."[261] It sparks tremendous motivation for their in-classroom learning, for sure. But that's just the cherry on top compared to the real-world impact that these products can have. Tackling something that no one, so far, has used technology to try to solve? "It is *so* powerful," says Laura.[262]

**

Slowly but steadily, AnnieCannons has gathered momentum. They offer each woman who graduates from the program immediate employment, either as subcontractors for their third-party clients or as teachers for the next cohort of students. For example, Claire began training to

---

261 Connel, Joanie. "Turning Tragedy into REAL Life: Empowering Survivors of Human Trafficking." Women Lead Radio, August 21, 2017. Connected Women of Influence (September 28, 2019).
262 Ibid.

become an AnnieCannons instructor after her graduation in the spring of 2019. Jessica says, "The hope is that, over the lifetime of AnnieCannons, the percentage of its staff that are survivors continually increases."[263] As of March 2019, they'd trained thirty-nine survivors, and twelve of them have stayed to work on projects outsourced from their client companies.[264]

Beyond the economic benefits, the women often enjoy the tech work more than they expect. "The majority come into the class having been conditioned to believe that this [computer science] is not for them and it's not something they'll be good at," Jessica says. "The best moment is always the first time someone is like, 'I could totally do this; this is fun.'"[265] For survivors who were trapped in such a degrading lifestyle for so long, becoming a professional in the tech industry completely turns the tide of their lives, opening up doors they'd never thought possible.

Also, being a software professional is "so much more empowering than only [being able] to use the label of

263 Hepburn, Stephanie. "AnnieCannons is Helping Human Trafficking Survivors Become Tech Experts." *Huffington Post,* October 19, 2017. Verizon Media (September 28, 2019).

264 Beer, Kieran. "Giving Victims of Sex Trafficking Their Due." *ACAMS Today,* March 28, 2019. Association of Certified Anti-Money Laundering Specialists (September 28, 2019).

265 Aguilera, Diana. "Human Rights at Home: How two alums are confronting slavery in their backyard." *Stanford Magazine,* September 6, 2017. Medium (September 28, 2018).

survivor," Laura explains.[266] It's not that anyone has to be ashamed of calling himself or herself a survivor... but sometimes that's the only identity that other people see. Annie-Cannons shows the survivors in their program that they can be *more* than that. Laura describes what it's like to see their students at a tech conference, networking with other attendees. Someone will ask them what they do, and "they say, 'I'm a web developer,' and then they look at us and smile," she says. When those moments happen, "It's the best outcome that we could hope for."[267]

We need more of these "best outcomes" for trafficking survivors in the United States and around the globe. It's actually quite shocking that as of 2017, AnnieCannons was "the only organization providing survivors with training in high-income skills."[268] It doesn't have to stay that way—hopefully, AnnieCannons' example will blaze the trail for more survivors to acquire marketable skills and realize the full potential of their talents. According to modern-slavery expert Kevin Bales, "[AnnieCannons is] one of the great things we've been missing."[269] It really does fill a critical gap

266 Connel, Joanie. "Turning Tragedy into REAL Life: Empowering Survivors of Human Trafficking." Women Lead Radio, August 21, 2017. Connected Women of Influence (September 28, 2019).

267 Ibid.

268 "Pitching Their Stories: AnnieCannons." *YouTube*, November 9, 2017. Solve—MIT (September 28, 2019).

269 Ryan, Kate. "Survivors draw on personal pasts to design anti-trafficking software." Reuters News Trust, February 21, 2019. Thomson Reuters Foundation (September 28, 2019).

in the rehabilitation process for survivors, providing economic empowerment for long-term independence.

And when we're contemplating how to leverage technology against trafficking, one of the most promising—and powerful—ways might be simply equipping survivors to take software into their own hands.

CHAPTER 8:

GET THE COMMUNITY INVOLVED

"The more of us that join together to fight this crime, the better the opportunity we have to eradicate it."

—KIMBERLY RITTER, EXCHANGE INITIATIVE[270]

Because human trafficking is a problem that entangles itself across country borders and cultural lines, it can't be eradicated by just one stakeholder. Law enforcement alone can't do it, neither can a cluster of nongovernmental organizations. As we tackle the problem from all angles—focusing

---

270 Scott, Katy. "Your hotel room photos could help catch sex traffickers." *The CNN Freedom Project*, March 20, 2017. CNN Business (September 28, 2019).

on the traffickers, the buyers, and the victims themselves—we also need to attack it with our collective forces, enlisting the entire community.

What excites me is that technology can facilitate new ways that allow people like you and me to join forces with stakeholders such as policymakers, law enforcement, and service providers. We've already seen some examples, like the Slavery from Space project where online volunteers labeled satellite images to train a machine-learning model, which in turn pinpoints possible sites of forced labor. Considering the power of social media and other online platforms to unite individuals across international communities, it's clear that there's tremendous potential in this area.

Let's dive into some of these projects that bring us together in the fight against human trafficking!

JUST FOUR PICTURES

"It took three days to find the girl."[271]

That's how Molly Hackett, principal of the St. Louis-based Nix Conference & Meeting Management corporation, described the tipping point that led to the development of TraffickCam—an app that began through a collaboration of local law enforcement, the hospitality industry, and computer

---

271 "Travelers use TraffickCam app to fight sex trafficking by uploading hotel room photos to national database." *Nix Assoc*, June 19, 2016. Nix Conference & Meeting Management (September 28, 2019).

science research, and now has thousands of people pitching in against sex trafficking in their own communities.

Together with co-principal Jane Quinn and senior account manager Kimberly Ritter, Hackett began crystallizing Nix's commitment to corporate social responsibility after their clients from the Federation of Sisters of St. Joseph asked them about the sex trafficking that happens in hotels.[272] It was something that they'd never thought about, but once these Catholic Sisters brought the issue to their attention, Ritter said, "We knew we couldn't tolerate this."[273] Almost immediately, they began to take steps to raise awareness within their sector.

Hackett, Quinn, and Ritter realized that their years of coordinating events for clients, from venue selection to registration logistics and everything in between, had placed them in a unique position to take a stand against this crime. In 2013, the women launched a social action organization called Exchange Initiative to "empower and inspire action among individuals and organizations to combat sex trafficking."[274] Through the Initiative, they offer resources for educators, youth, parents, and employees in the travel industry, enabling them to more consciously spot warning signs, prevent unsafe

---

272 Miska, Rhonda. "Q & A with Kimberly Ritter, fighting human trafficking with a smartphone app." *Global Sisters Report*, January 12, 2017. National Catholic Reporter (September 28, 2019).

273 Ibid.

274 "Exchange Initiative: Real Resources to End Sex Trafficking." *Exchange Initiative*, 2019. Exchange Initiative (September 28, 2019).

situations, and report suspicions of sex trafficking to the appropriate authorities.

As part of the work, the members of the Exchange Initiative also began guiding investigators of sex trafficking cases.[275] It turns out that expertise in the travel industry was sorely needed, as the hotels posed a particular problem for local law enforcement. Here was their quandary: the photos that traffickers post in online ads are often taken inside the hotel rooms where they keep their victims. The investigators had access to these images, but pinpointing which hotel could possibly correspond to each photograph was like trying to find a needle in a haystack. But with Nix's extensive experience in hotels across the country, they could better match different hotels to their interior room layouts. Working closely with investigators, Molly Hackett and her team painstakingly worked through cases to narrow down possible hotels as quickly and accurately as possible, identifying features including bed linens, lamps, and curtains.

However, even the best human expertise had its limits. One day, Molly remembered that "we couldn't identify a motel room. We connected the vice squad with our associates in that city, but it took three days to find the girl."[276] In these kinds of investigations, time is of the essence: in

275 "TraffickCam FAQ." *Exchange Initiative*, 2019. Exchange Initiative (September 28, 2019).
276 "Travelers use TraffickCam app to fight sex trafficking by uploading hotel room photos to national database." *Nix Assoc*, June 19, 2016. Nix Conference & Meeting Management (September 28, 2019).

the hours (or days) spent identifying a hotel room, the trafficker can easily relocate their victims before law enforcement arrives. Even a short delay is unacceptable. In Molly's mind, three days "seemed way too long, given today's technology."[277]

After that incident, she began brainstorming ideas for an app that investigators could use to expedite their response to sex trafficking cases. The next step was finding someone who could turn it into reality...

It turns out that the answer was just a few miles away.

At Washington University in St. Louis, Dr. Robert Pless and his research associate Abby Stylianou had already gotten their hands dirty in the crime-fighting world. "Back in 2013," Abby said in a university interview, "we actually consulted with the St. Louis Police Department to use computer vision to track down the location of a lost grave [of a 1983 crime victim]."[278] They'd located the grave by analyzing photographs of the burial, using artificial intelligence techniques to identify where the photos had been taken.

After the lost grave project, Abby was recruited into the prestigious FBI Citizens Academy program, where she glimpsed an insider's view of the role of federal law enforcement in the community. It was coincidentally the same week they were discussing sex trafficking in the academy when an

---

277 Ibid.
278 "Developing TraffickCam: Inside the Research | Washington University." *YouTube*, September 1, 2016. Washington University in St. Louis (September 28, 2019).

unexpected opportunity called her name. She remembers, "*The St. Louis Post-Dispatch* ran a story about this idea that a local group had to create an application… to take pictures of hotel rooms so that law enforcement could then search through, to figure out where victims of sex trafficking were being photographed."[279] It was right up her alley—she was all in.

Exchange Initiative had the idea, and Dr. Pless's research lab had the capacity to make it happen. "So that's how we got involved in building TraffickCam," Abby said with a smile.

"TraffickCam is two parts," Dr. Pless explains. "One is an app that allows anybody to contribute pictures of hotel rooms that they're in."[280] The researchers included these pictures in a training dataset that included over one million images from 50,000 hotels and 92 major hotel chains across the country. They used this dataset through a deep neural network, which basically helps the computer algorithm learn a set of filters to identify matching images. Then, as more people submit photos through the app, the algorithm can process new images using the same patterns it learned from the training dataset. And with each photograph, it becomes a little bit smarter. All of this information is channeled into the second part of the app, which Dr. Pless describes as "a portal where law enforcement [who] want to find out what hotel [a picture] comes

---

279 Ibid.
280 Ibid.

from, can upload the picture, and it's compared against all
the images in the database in order to find the match."[281] That
way, law enforcement can get fast and accurate indications
for where they should direct their operations on the ground.

Throughout the development process, the Exchange
Initiative may not have worked on the technical aspects of
the platform, but they made the strategic connections with
donors, law enforcement, and public awareness in order to
ensure that the app would be successful. Private donations
came in through the non-profit St. Louis Community Foundation, and Catholic Sisters again played a part, with the local
Congregation of the Sisters of St. Joseph agreeing to match
every dollar given to Exchange Initiative up to $100,000.
Each gift helped make the app possible.

With its launch by the Exchange Initiative in June 2016,
the TraffickCam app became available for anyone to download to their mobile device for free. From there, it's a simple
process to add photos to the national database, which is called
Hotels-50K. "You just enter your hotel room and your room
number. You take four pictures, and you submit them to
the website," said Abby. "And then those become part of the
pipeline that law enforcement can use to track down where
the victims are being trafficked." The photos don't have to be
professional—in fact, the researchers don't prefer high-qual-
ity images from travel websites. In their recently published

---

281 Ibid.

paper (2019), they noted that crowd-sourced photos tend to be more similar to the images in sex ads because they're taken on "similar devices, at varying orientations, with luggage and other clutter, and without professional lighting."[282] This helps the algorithm more accurately draw connections between the photos in the dataset and the images used in the investigations.

When a law enforcement agency has a photo ad of a sex trafficking victim, they can run it against the portal to figure out where the photo could have been taken. Every detail, from the patterns in the carpet to the view out the window, are analyzed by computer vision algorithms that match the image against the database to generate "a list of potential hotels where the photo may have been taken."[283] Based on early testing, TraffickCam was shown to be eighty-five percent accurate in identifying the correct hotel within the top twenty matches.

Before the app could be rolled out to law enforcement agencies across the United States, it was beta tested by Sergeant Adam Kavanaugh and the St. Louis County Police Department. As the Supervisor of the St. Louis County Multi-Jurisdictional Human Trafficking Task Force, Kava-

---

282 Stylianou et al. "Hotels-50K: A Global Hotel Recognition Dataset." *arXiv*, January 26, 2017. Association for the Advancement of Artificial Intelligence (September 28, 2019).

283 "Travelers use TraffickCam app to fight sex trafficking by uploading hotel room photos to national database." *Nix Assoc*, June 19, 2016. Nix Conference & Meeting Management (September 28, 2019).

naugh recognized the incredible potential of this new technology. "The app," he said, "will give law enforcement yet another technological tool to [recover victims and locate suspects] in a quicker, more proficient manner when investigating cases involving human trafficking and child exploitation."[284] He hopes that it will help make investigators' jobs both safer and easier.

So far, hundreds of law enforcement agencies have put TraffickCam to use, including human trafficking investigators with the non-profit National Center for Missing and Exploited Children (NCMEC). It gives them an extra edge because it helps trace the link between victims and locations, verifying "where victims have been trafficked, and where their traffickers might move them or others in the future."[285] As more and more people use the application, its intelligence will only continue to improve. The larger the dataset, the more accurate the algorithm.

As for future goals, Exchange Initiative and the WUSTL researchers continue to refine the app and database. "We are hoping to scale up the volume of data that we train on by a factor of 10," Abby says.[286] The Exchange Initiative website adds, "We also have received interest from law

284 Ibid.
285 Stylianou et al. "Hotels-50K: A Global Hotel Recognition Dataset." *arXiv*, January 26, 2017. Association for the Advancement of Artificial Intelligence (September 28, 2019).
286 "Using AI To Stop Child Trafficking." *NVIDIA News Center*, February 22, 2019. NVIDIA (September 28, 2019).

enforcement internationally. Our focus now is on the United States but we hope to expand to other countries in the future."[287] For example, Kimberly Ritter said, "We have had inquiries from Interpol and from other countries who would like to have access to the database."[288] Their overarching goal is to encourage as much global participation as possible.

As of 2019, the Exchange Initiative still welcomes donations to support the maintenance and development of TraffickCam, with the Congregation of the Sisters of St. Joseph agreeing to match every donated dollar up to $100,000. Dr. Pless and Stylianou are researching ways to make use of the images that are uploaded to the database from smartphone cameras. And the word continues to spread about TraffickCam: it's been publicized hundreds of times on news outlets such as *The Huffington Post*, the *Washington Post*, and *PBS Nova*, as well as on social media platforms like Twitter and Facebook.

Perhaps the most powerful part of TraffickCam is the way it enables anyone to join the fight. Increased awareness has led to increased participation: currently, more than 2.9 million photos of over 250,000 hotels have been uploaded from more than 152,000 devices, representing every major metropolitan area in the United States. "This is an issue that

287 "TraffickCam FAQ." *Exchange Initiative*, 2019. Exchange Initiative (September 28, 2019).

288 Miska, Rhonda. "Q & A with Kimberly Ritter, fighting human trafficking with a smartphone app." *Global Sisters Report*, January 12, 2017. National Catholic Reporter (September 28, 2019).

people really care about and feel sort of helpless that there's nothing that they can do…" Abby said, "so it's been really, really nice for us to provide this sense of empowerment that just by taking four pictures of your hotel room, you can do something to actually, legitimately, make a difference."[289] Whether on vacation, traveling for work, with a sports team or with family, anyone can play a part in eradicating local sex trafficking with just a few clicks of their smartphone.

SEEING THE UNSEEN

Another UK group that's getting the community involved in combating slavery is Unseen UK, the organization that Phil Bennett volunteered with for years as a Salesforce employee. The charity was created in 2008 by a small team of ambitious individuals, including social justice adviser Andrew Wallis, schoolteacher Kate Garbers, and deputy police and crime commissioner Justine Currell. They each confronted the horrors of modern-day slavery and realized they couldn't keep living like they didn't care about the thousands of individuals enslaved in their own country and around the world: "It was real. It was happening in our streets. We couldn't ignore it, we wanted to respond."[290] So they decided to come together to see what they could do to help.

289 "Developing TraffickCam: Inside the Research | Washington University." *YouTube*, September 1, 2016. Washington University in St. Louis (September 28, 2019).

290 "Our People." *Unseen*, 2019. Unseen UK (September 28, 2019).

As a registered charity in the United Kingdom, Unseen concentrates on three main areas: supporting survivors, equipping anti-slavery activists, and overturning the systems that keep slavery hidden. Their vision? Exposing the "unseen" so that it can be eradicated. They've set up safe houses for men, women, and children all over the UK, providing immediate support for survivors from all backgrounds. They collaborate with a tech company that hosts a Central Registry for business transparency statements in order to facilitate greater accountability between consumers, investors, and companies. And they manage a Modern Slavery Helpline that reaches all across the UK, allowing anyone to call in to report concerns of a potential slavery situation.

The Helpline launched in autumn of 2016, the result of close communication with local city council, police, social service agencies, and—of course—their founding partner, the BT Group. A British multinational telecommunications company, BT had already demonstrated their commitment to fighting modern-day slavery by setting up a Modern Slavery Working Group in 2015 to concentrate their efforts on eliminating modern slavery in their business and supply chain. They had also invited Unseen staff to train BT procurement and recruitment teams on ways that they can detect and combat human trafficking in their day-to-day responsibilities. Now, they combined forces to debut the Helpline with massive publicity campaigns. In fact, Unseen and BT worked so well together that their partnership was nominated for the "Corporate National Partnership Champion" at the 2017 Charity Times Awards.

Although they'd made the Helpline accessible through phone calls and webform submissions, the folks at Unseen knew that they could expand its impact if they made it easier than ever for the entire community to get involved. As modern-day slavery is "rarely reported by the victims themselves but are normally reported by third parties or discovered by police investigations...it [was] vital to increase public awareness," which would, in turn, increase the frequency of third-party tips about suspicious situations.[291] "We know increased awareness and action from the public is critical to turning the tide on modern slavery," said Eric Anderson, Head of the Modern Slavery Programme at BT.[292] That's why Unseen and BT began brainstorming how to encourage citizens to make use of the Helpline.

How about an app?

The idea for an app actually grew out of BT's annual company-wide tournament called the "Challenge Cup," where employees are challenged to "come up with a business idea to improve the lives of our customers."[293] One of the entries

---

291 "Unseen App rolled out across North Wales." *North Wales Police News and Appeals*, December 21, 2018. North Wales Police (September 28, 2019).

292 "Unseen Launches App to Report Modern Slavery." *Unseen News*, July 30, 2018. Unseen UK (September 28, 2019).

293 "British Telecommunications plc: Modern Slavery Act Transparency Statement 2017/18." *BT Digital Impact and Sustainability: Human Rights*, 2018. BT plc (September 28, 2019).

encapsulated a vision for an app that would empower its users to spot situations of modern-day slavery and then act upon it, reporting their tips directly to the Helpline.

The first component was education. Using infographics, the app "details both physical and psychological signs to be aware of in victims and provides details of the environments they may be found in," explains Richard Sidney, Detective Sergeant of the North Wales Police's Modern Slavery Unit.[294] For instance, users learn that forced labor abuses are mostly found in industries such as the agricultural, manufacturing, and construction sectors. Then, the app "summarises legislation which assists law enforcement agencies, victims and commercial organisations and even provides a direct link to the government website which includes the legislation definitions."[295] It's comprehensive, user-friendly, and actionable.

Beyond helping users understand what modern-day slavery looks like, the app then provides a communication channel that feeds information back into the Modern Slavery Helpline. This way, users can directly and confidentially inform authorities about red flags that they are now trained to notice. Whether they're a victim or a bystander, those who have been "unable or unwilling to come forward" can

---

294 "Unseen App rolled out across North Wales." *North Wales Police News and Appeals*, December 21, 2018. North Wales Police (September 28, 2019).

295 Ibid.

easily reach out to report a situation of possible slavery... with just the click of a button.[296] That data could then be used to inform police investigations, court proceedings, and victim services, sometimes contributing significantly to the outcome of a case.

The Unseen App went live on July 30, 2018—a fitting day, recognized as World Day Against Trafficking by the United Nations. It is available for free download from Windows, iTunes, and Google Play app stores. As Eric Anderson says, "It's there in your pocket when you need it."[297]

The great thing is, this is not "just another app" sitting in the app store that no one knows about. On the contrary: in true "wrap the app" fashion, Unseen has tirelessly promoted their mobile app to invite as many users as they can. On the app's launch day, they partnered with PMP Recruitment, a staffing company with years of experience across the workforce, to launch a campaign called "Be Seen, Be Heard: Tackling modern slavery in high volume recruitment."[298] A major facet of the campaign included high-visibility items such as jackets, wristbands, key fobs, pens, car stickers, etc. to support Unseen and the helpline. They also encouraged the

---

296 "Unseen, Modern Slavery Helpline: Annual Assessment 2018." *Modern Slavery Helpline*, 2018. Unseen UK and the Modern Slavery Helpline (September 28, 2019).

297 "Unseen Launches App to Report Modern Slavery." *Unseen News*, July 30, 2018. Unseen UK (September 28, 2019).

298 "Support Unseen / Be Seen Be Heard." *Unseen*, 2018. Unseen UK (September 28, 2019).

promotion of the Modern Slavery Helpline and the Unseen App through social media via specific hashtags.

When Phil Bennett told me about the app, he attributed its success to these strong partnerships that Unseen has built across the workforce, not the least of which is law enforcement. Although we tend to think of law enforcement as the authorities who deal with human trafficking cases, in reality, police officers also need the education and resources to be able to appropriately respond to modern-day slavery on the job. It's encouraging to see police forces all over the UK rolling out the app to their officers and staff. For example, the police in North Wales downloaded the Unseen App so that they would have the tools to effectively identify and support potential trafficking victims on the frontlines. Sergeant Richard Sidney says that "it's a simple resource which utilises technology that is already in place, so it is easy to implement."[299] And he sees the value of the app in all work environments, adding, "I would encourage any organisation or business who provide smart devices to their workforce to push the App out to each device to help raise awareness of this issue."[300]

In the first six months of the app's launch, the Helpline received seventy submissions—not just from the UK but internationally as well. In 2018 overall, Unseen reported that

299 "Unseen App rolled out across North Wales." *North Wales Police News and Appeals*, December 21, 2018. North Wales Police (September 28, 2019).

300 Ibid.

7,121 victims had been identified via the Helpline, thanks to tips from phone calls, web forms, and app submissions. That's forty-six percent more than the previous year.[301] Hopefully, these numbers will continue to rise as the app gathers more users who will engage with the Helpline.

"Your report could mean somebody's freedom," the Unseen staff believe—and it really is true. On their website, they share a composite case story of a young Polish woman called Anna, whose experience is representative of many survivors. Anna had been trafficked by her boyfriend for both sex and labor, trapped for four years until a woman gave her the phone number for the Modern Slavery Helpline. "I eventually found the courage to call and tell them about what was happening to me," she remembers.[302] The staff offered her 24/7 support over the phone until the police were able to raid the nail salon where she worked. Then, Anna said that "Unseen's Resettlement and Outreach service helped me to find accommodation, access legal support and attend lessons to improve my English."[303] She never forgot the lady who empowered her to report her situation. "She gave me the key which unlocked my freedom."[304]

---

301 "Unseen, Modern Slavery Helpline: Annual Assessment 2018." *Modern Slavery Helpline*, 2018. Unseen UK and the Modern Slavery Helpline (September 28, 2019).

302 "Our Impact / Modern Slavery is Real—Survivor Stories." *Unseen*, 2019. Unseen UK (September 28, 2019).

303 Ibid.

304 Ibid.

In the end, that's what motivates the staff at Unseen and BT: knowing that as they bring the community together on this issue, their work could help change someone's life. Eric Anderson of BT adds, "If just one victim of modern slavery uses our app—or gets help because someone else has used it—then every single moment of our time spent developing it has been worth it."[305] He personally may never meet the people he's impacted, but he's content knowing that somewhere, because of this technology, somebody *sees* them.

A PLACE TO SPEND THE NIGHT

Along with contributing to victim identification, community members also have a chance to assist in the process of recovery after victims have been removed from immediate danger. This is a crucial component of anti-trafficking work, yet one that sometimes fails to be adequately addressed. After the initial intervention to disrupt the trafficking situation, there's so much coordination that needs to happen. Where will the survivor find resources? Will she be able to combat the stigma and shame surrounding her in order to forge a new life? Will she be in danger if her trafficker is still out there? Will she want to take her case to court? Or will she end up returning to the same situation she just left?

---

305 Green, Chloe. "Charity develops slavery reporting app." *Charity Digital News: Impact & Efficiency*, August 6, 2018. Charity Digital (September 28, 2019).

Usually the most immediate question is, *Where should she sleep tonight?*

In the United States, at least, the main problem isn't that the resources don't exist. It's that local victim service providers aren't able to communicate with each other in order to utilize those resources to their fullest potential. With so many other pressing legal and social issues to deal with, the last headache they need is prolonged communication about who has space to take in the survivor. It takes a gazillion phone calls, and then if the shelters are full, they turn to Plan B: figuring out how to cover the cost of a hotel stay by calling up donors or digging into their own budget.

Cori Manthorne, program director of a domestic violence agency called Community Overcoming Relationship Abuse (CORA) in San Mateo, California, underscores the urgency of the problem. "The last thing we ever want to tell them is we don't have a safe place for you to sleep," she says.[306] However, out of the 1000+ requests for shelter that CORA receives each year via their twenty-four-hour hotline, their safe houses only have the capacity to fill 200 of those requests. What about the other 800?

"It's not okay that people don't have a safe place to spend the night," says Marnie Webb, CEO of a tech group called

---

306 Martin, Allen. "Mobile App Connects Victims of Violence With Safe Spaces." *San Francisco CBS Local*, November 18, 2015. CBS Broadcasting Inc. (September 28, 2019).

Caravan Studios.[307] It's a division of a San Francisco non-profit called TechSoup where Marnie also serves as the Chief Community Impact Officer. Shaking her head at how such a basic necessity could be so difficult to come by, she explained that the problem first came to her attention when her mother-in-law told her about a woman who needed a place to stay. Her mother-in-law had said, "I'd pay for a hotel room for that girl if I could." And Marnie, who's spent her career overseeing technology projects for social good, thought, "Wait a second! How can we put this together?"[308]

In reality, Caravan Studios' Chief Technology Officer Anna Jaeger emphasizes that it was much more involved than a simple lightbulb moment: "This idea did not come to us overnight."[309] Rather, it arose out of the on-the-ground, need-focused approach that sets TechSoup apart as an innovator making real impact. With over thirteen years of close relationships with domestic violence agencies in California, as an organization "we really believe in working with community to design responses to their issues," Anna explains, which means they take the time to truly understand the problems that local nonprofits are dealing with.[310] Only

307 Ibid.
308 Ibid.
309 Jaeger, Anna and Keith Thode. "Webinar—Developing Mobile Apps from Idea to Launch: A Case Study." *YouTube*, August 23, 2013. Tech-Soup Global (September 28, 2019).
310 Ibid.

after they get a sense of these issues, will they "discuss these in sessions called 'generators' to look for opportunities for technical intervention."[311] Marnie Webb adds, "We aren't case managers, we're technologists and so we wanted a lot of validation that we weren't creating any unintended consequences."[312] The idea for SafeNight app was thus born "out of all those conversations, those years of conversations with domestic violence organizations."[313] It's a perfect example of starting with a need rather than a solution.

The Caravan Studios team believed that the shelter predicament could be resolved with a mobile smartphone app. But it also took some discussion before they landed on a design that would be most useful. Initially, they'd thought of creating "a bed-finder app where shelters that are full can reach out to other shelters and say, 'Do you have a bed that will meet my needs?'"[314] When they pitched the idea to the nonprofit community of domestic violence agencies, however, this was their response: "You know, that's lovely but most of our shelters are full. Skip the bed-finder part. Go straight to the hotel rooms because that's what is going to increase our

311 Ibid.
312 Thomas, Emily. "Human Trafficking Survivors Find Safe Haven Through Mobile App." *Bay Area Bandwidth*, October 2, 2016. Medium (September 28, 2019).
313 Jaeger, Anna and Keith Thode. "Webinar—Developing Mobile Apps from Idea to Launch: A Case Study." *YouTube*, August 23, 2013. Tech-Soup Global (September 28, 2019).
314 Ibid.

capacity."[315] So, Anna remembers, "We shifted. We changed the focus of the app to be this more fundraising type of app, crowd-sourced fundraising for hotel rooms."[316] Thanks to TechSoup's dedication to cultivating strong, intimate connections with these nonprofits, they were able to hone their efforts on a design that these organizations would actually use and appreciate—and a design that would also engage the entire community.

With a generous grant from Microsoft as well as other strategic funding initiatives through TechSoup's inter-organizational relationships, Caravan Studios called up their longstanding partner, Aidmatrix, a Dallas-based software developer non-profit. Aidmatrix didn't hesitate, agreeing to handle the technical aspects of the app development. Keith Thode, COO and Chief Technology Officer of Aidmatrix at the time, explained that they followed a common software development process known as "waterfall," where "you do all the planning upfront, then the requirement, then the design, then the development, then the testing, then the acceptance."[317] From the back end of the fundraising engine (which they borrowed from web-based fundraising infrastructure from a previous virtual food drive project) to the logo itself, at every step the developers focused on what would be the most straightforward, most user-friendly, and

---

315 Ibid.
316 Ibid.
317 Ibid.

ultimately a solution that would leverage existing resources to their fullest potential.

The goals of their design are twofold: (1) to find shelter, and (2) to fund shelter if necessary. The first part of the platform is Safe Shelter Collaborative, a platform that kicks into action when a survivor, or someone on behalf of them (such as a family member or local police), contacts a sheltering agency. A case manager from the nonprofit agency, which has been screened by TechSoup, will log into the Safe Shelter Collaborative (SSC) network, enter the survivor's demographic information such as gender, age, and any mental health or substance abuse issues, to search for available shelters nearby. Representatives from these shelters respond if they have room to appropriately accommodate the client. From there, the case manager can call those who responded "maybe" or "yes" to discuss more details. "It has streamlined our work, instead of taking hours and days to find emergency housing it takes 1-2 calls on average," one agency reports.[318] By reducing the time spent contacting shelters that are already full—from hours to minutes—SSC makes everyone's lives easier, helping them use their time and energy most efficiently.

If no shelter has capacity? "In the same city where the shelter may be full," Keith says, "there may be a hotel room that's about to go empty. Well, you know, can't we bridge those two

---

318 "Safe Shelter Collaborative." *Caravan Studios*, 2018. TechSoup (September 28, 2019).

things?"[319] As an example, Cora Manthorne explains that her agency has built relationships with hotels over the years, so "in that case, we say, 'We have this hotel available for you,' So there are immediate results for their safety."[320] However, the issue is funding these hotel stays, which may need to be extended indefinitely depending on the situation.

That's where the software really shines... and where the community comes in!

Anyone can become a supporter simply by downloading the SafeNight app, which is available on Windows Phone Store, Google Play, or the AppStore. Then, when a nonprofit has to place a client into a hotel, they'll push out an alert requesting support. Community members who've selected that agency through SafeNight will "receive a notification that an individual is in need, and then they'll have an opportunity to help cover the cost of the hotel room via the app."[321] It's a one-time, tax-deductible donation through PayPal. Donors and survivors remain anonymous to each other, but even so, donors have the satisfaction of knowing that they've helped someone take the next step forward. "No matter where they

---

319 Jaeger, Anna and Keith Thode. "Webinar—Developing Mobile Apps from Idea to Launch: A Case Study." *YouTube*, August 23, 2013. Tech-Soup Global (September 28, 2019).

320 Martin, Allen. "Mobile App Connects Victims of Violence With Safe Spaces." *San Francisco CBS Local*, November 18, 2015. CBS Broadcasting Inc. (September 28, 2019).

321 Jaeger, Anna and Keith Thode. "Webinar—Developing Mobile Apps from Idea to Launch: A Case Study." *YouTube*, August 23, 2013. Tech-Soup Global (September 28, 2019).

are or what they're doing, they can be a part of making a difference in that family's life at that moment," says Jennifer Morrison, who coordinated SafeNight development within Aidmatrix's spinoff venture called AdvanceNet Labs.[322]

Beginning around 2013, Caravan Studios worked with the national non-profit Polaris Project to pilot Safe Shelter Collaborative in California, Texas, Iowa, and New Jersey, where the staff of domestic violence and trafficking victim service provider agencies received training on how to use the app effectively. They unrolled the app gradually, gathering feedback from the nonprofits through close communication until they had a robust solution to offer the community at large.

The app officially launched in 2016. Now, it serves organizations all across the United States, including Community Advocates for Family and Youth (CAFY) in Maryland. In CAFY's case, founder and executive director Arleen Joell had spent five years developing relationships with hotels for emergency stays, but the uncertain duration of the stays always made coordination tricky. "If someone had to leave immediately for fear of threat, harm or sanity, we always had to say, 'Okay, what's the game plan?' because we could only do one night and sometimes three," she explains.[323] Now,

---

322 Wigglesworth, Valerie. "SafeNight app comes to the aid of domestic violence victims in North Texas." *Dallas News*, October 10, 2015. The Dallas Morning News (September 28, 2019).

323 Kyles, Akira. "Local Organization Launches App to Keep Domestic Violence Survivors Safe." *AFRO: The Black Media Authority*, July 14, 2018. The AFRO-American Newspapers (September 28, 2019).

SafeNight allows them to extend that stay by engaging the community's support, with about fifty participating donors in 2018. It's been a complete game-changer.

Where does the community come in?

This is crowdfunding at its finest. "The community wants to help!" Marnie Webb says.[324] Through careful collaboration, Caravan Studios found a way to make it happen. One donor, Shelagh Casey Brown, shared how the app is impacting her own life. "You want to be able to help and yet you don't know how," she explained. "Now... you sign up for [SafeNight] app and you can make a difference and you know you have."[325] With everyone involved, we can make strides in ending human trafficking in our societies. Marnie Webb says that these issues of trafficking and domestic violence "get solved because a community comes together and they say not here, no more."[326] And SafeNight enables them to channel that indignation into a real impact.

For me, SafeNight embodies the power of technology to bring out our society's full potential. As it links shelters, hotels, and the broader community, it eases survivors'

---

324 Martin, Allen. "Mobile App Connects Victims of Violence With Safe Spaces." *San Francisco CBS Local*, November 18, 2015. CBS Broadcasting Inc. (September 28, 2019).

325 Wilkins, Tracee and Gina Cook. "App Helps Victims of Domestic Violence Find Safe Place to Stay." *NBC Washington*, August 15, 2018. NCB4 TV (September 28, 2019).

326 Thomas, Emily. "Human Trafficking Survivors Find Safe Haven Through Mobile App." *Bay Area Bandwidth*, October 2, 2016. Medium (September 28, 2019).

transition from violence to safety and from slavery to freedom. "A safe shelter is just the first thing that they need in the support to exercise choice and control over their lives again," says Marnie Webb.[327] Providing that first thing? "It's tremendous to be in a position to be able to do that."[328]

**

From identifying victims to catching warning signs to supporting survivors, there are so many areas of anti-trafficking work where technology can serve as a platform to bring the community into the fight. If you're able to download an app, consider contributing to one of these crowd-sourcing projects. And if you're pursuing tech development, brainstorm ways to include a larger set of users in the anti-trafficking mission.

Law enforcement, social workers, and survivors themselves may deal with the immediate face of the crime, but human trafficking happens in our *communities*: where we live and work and gather.

Let's combat it on the same level.

---

327 Ibid.
328 Martin, Allen. "Mobile App Connects Victims of Violence With Safe Spaces." *San Francisco CBS Local*, November 18, 2015. CBS Broadcasting Inc. (September 28, 2019).

PART 3:

ENVISIONING THE FUTURE

"Having hope means looking forward to tomorrow, knowing the sun will rise and the day that lies ahead is one full of freedom."

—INTERNATIONAL JUSTICE MISSION

CHAPTER 9:

TURNING IDEAS INTO IMPACT

———

"There are a lot of cool ideas out there, but the gap between taking a cool idea and making it into something that's actually having an impact can be pretty big."

—ROBERT BEISER, EXECUTIVE DIRECTOR
OF SEATTLE AGAINST SLAVERY

People usually plunge into anti-trafficking work heart-first, seeing or hearing something that makes them want to *do something.*

Take the time that the Department of Homeland Security (DHS) called Ashton Kutcher's fledgling organization, Thorn, asking for help to rescue a seven-year-old girl, whose images of sexual abuse pervaded the dark web. "They'd watched her for three years, and they could not find the perpetrator," Kutcher remembers.[329] Hearing her plight broke his heart.

Stories like these are what spawn ideas, the seeds of innovation. Surely there's no shortage of them.

For Kutcher, it meant dismantling child sex trafficking with its own weapon: technology. "For the next three months, I had to go to sleep every night and think about that little girl that was still being abused," he said, "and that fact that if I built the right thing, we could save her."[330] It devastated him, driving him and his team to develop the tools that law enforcement needed to analyze data on the dark web.

Oftentimes, people will have useful ideas for harnessing technology to tackle a piece of the problem… but getting those ideas off the ground? That's where it can get tricky. With uncertainty and unexpected hurdles along the way, it's no wonder that so many ambitious projects fall by the wayside.

If we want to ensure that our efforts won't end in a gust of hot air, we'll need to carefully consider what it will take to bring our ideas to life.

IDEA IS NOT IMPACT

When I talked with Robert Beiser, the executive director of Seattle Against Slavery, he described some of the challenges

---

329 "Ashton Kutcher Speech on Human Trafficking Before Congress." *YouTube*, February 15, 2017. ABC News (September 28, 2019).
330 Ibid.

he's seen in anti-slavery work around the world, particularly when it comes to bringing technology into the anti-trafficking sphere. "Some of it's a little challenging because people will come up with ideas first off, that isn't the same as what an effective intervention is," he said. "There are a lot of cool ideas out there, but the gap between taking a cool idea and making it into something that's actually having an impact can be pretty big."

For example, Robert asked me to imagine having a brilliant machine-learning algorithm that confidently identifies a fourteen-year-old girl who's in an ad for sex. "What's the response mechanism that you're going to tie that to, that'll have someone going and meeting up with that person?" he continued, piling on the questions. "Okay, where are they? Tulsa, Oklahoma. What do we do? Who do we know there, who will respond?" When he framed it that way, programming the machine-learning model suddenly seemed like the easy part.

Robert's distinction between idea and impact reminded me of intelligence analyst Justin Underwood's definition of intelligence: it's *actionable information*. In today's world, data is everywhere. If it's not used at all, we'll be wasting our time, and if it's misused, we could end up doing more harm than good. But often, the most helpful solutions involve leveraging the data that's out there, and then connecting the right resources so that those on the ground can actually *do* something with it. "Sometimes it's the physical linkup of the things that you can do with technology" that makes all the difference, Robert told me. "You have to go a step further, and it takes a lot of work to figure out how to make that piece successful."

Yes, it's tough, but it's possible. And it's extremely crucial!

We could spend hours discussing strategies for carrying an idea from the brainstorming session to the frontlines, but here are just a few key themes:

- We must seek to engage with the **perspective** of victims, survivor advocates, and other stakeholders who will be using the technology, in order to design it suitably for their needs.

- We must scope out strategic **partnerships** for support, fresh angles, and to ensure effective deployment in the real world.

- Even when we encounter obstacles along the way—and we will, whether from systemic factors beyond our control, or from our own internal struggles—we must rebound, reassess, and **persevere**.

- What ultimately keeps us going? Holding onto the **promise** of a future free from slavery, where every man and woman, boy and girl, lives without doubting their dignity. *That's* how we'll bring an idea from potential to pay off.

PERSPECTIVE

With any kind of technology, it's critical to design every detail of the platform with the users in mind. Among a host of considerations, we must think about which devices or social media platforms they prefer, when and where they would use our technology, how they would interact with it, and what kind of barriers might prevent them from utilizing it. A user-centered perspective is key to creating a product that will actually make an impact.

This theme emerges in the partnership between Seattle Against Slavery (SAS), a non-profit organization that innovates anti-trafficking technology, and Real Escape from the Sex Trade (REST), a victim service provider organization in Seattle. Their mission to develop an automatic text messaging platform for victim reach-out wonderfully illustrates both the intricacies and challenges of the user-centered approach.

Throughout the process, SAS and REST had to overcome inevitable disconnects in terms of designing specific features. Liz Rush, the technology director for SAS, admits that the software developers don't have all the right answers on their own, even if they're truly trying to design what's best for the survivors. "We have ideological beliefs that drive some of the design built into our software," she explains. Engineers often prioritize values such as efficiency and automation. So, oftentimes there are details that they wouldn't even think about but make a huge difference from the survivors' standpoint.

Here's a common example that Liz shared: "[A volunteer will say,] 'Oh, I have this great idea, we can improve it in this way.' And then we'll go to one of the survivor advocates on our platform and be like, 'Hey, what do you think about this idea?' And they'll be like, 'I don't care about that... But what I *do* care about is x, y, and z.' So then we prioritize those things first."

For example, volunteers have pitched the idea of adding an automatic follow-up feature, which sends another text if there is no reply after twenty-four hours. "It sounds good... to retry if we don't hear back," Liz says, "but from the survivor perspective... really the person who has to be in charge of the process is the victim." For situations with survivors of commercial sexual exploitation and domestic violence, agency is critical. "You have to empower the victim to make the choices about their life because that's often the thing that's taken away from them: the ability to choose," Liz explains. "We don't want to automatically keep bothering someone. We want to offer help and let that person decide if they want to have a relationship with us or not."

Follow up *is* extremely important, though. REST's Outreach Coordinator Jackie Loos told me that she follows through with people who respond to the text messages, not with automatically generated responses but in a genuinely relational way. She'll offer to buy them lunch, meet them in person, or ask if they can set up a phone call. There's a lot that can be misconstrued over text, she said, and building trust is key.

While automatic text follow up wasn't the best idea, Jackie did give some examples of features that she did find helpful. She liked the ability to delete or archive texts, as well as to name and flag certain messages to make them easier to find later. She also wanted to be able to get alerts on her phone when she wasn't at her computer. Another huge feature that she asked the technologists to add was an "away" message that would be sent out automatically if someone responds to a text and she can't get back to them right away. "They need to know they're acknowledged," she said, because that window of time where victims are willing and able to reach out for help can be very small. If she doesn't respond quickly enough, she may have lost her chance to connect with them.

Whenever she has feedback about the user interface or if something isn't going right, Jackie communicates directly with the tech team; they're able to exchange ideas, implement changes, and engage with each other in a flexible, collaborative way. And Liz told me that it's been invaluable to have "had survivor advocates using the platform [from the very beginning] so that they could give us feedback on what was useful, what was not useful, what was realistic, what wasn't realistic…" By understanding each other's perspectives, they've striven to develop software platforms that are aligned with the reality of sex trafficking and serve survivors most effectively.

PARTNERSHIPS

Another absolute must for successful anti-trafficking tech projects is cultivating intentional partnerships, bringing together a diversity of talents and resources on all levels, from interpersonal relationships to cross-sector collaborations. Even if we have a great idea, it won't be useful unless we can connect it with the actors who can:

- *support* it, like donors or private foundations
- *develop* it, like software engineers and research scientists
- *promote* it, like advocacy organizations and representatives
- and *use* it, like victim service providers, law enforcement, or policymakers.

At the end of the day, it really is a team effort!

For example, the folks at Thorn, Ashton Kutcher's organization that creates technological tools to combat child sex trafficking, relied on Arizona State University's McCain Institute for financial support while they were creating Spotlight, a tool that helps law enforcement identify children whose faces appear in sexually abusive materials. For the actual software development, they received help from a Tennessee-based company called Digital Reasoning, whose engineers offered to work pro bono to help turn raw data from the dark web into actionable information.[331]

Then, of course, Thorn had to work closely with the police to deploy the technology so that they would actually be able to use it to accelerate their operations. This on-the-ground collaboration ensured that Thorn's solutions would be integrated into existing frameworks; otherwise, the technology

---

331 "Ashton Kutcher Speech on Human Trafficking Before Congress." *YouTube*, February 15, 2017. ABC News (September 28, 2019).

wouldn't be as effective. "Continue to foster these private/ public partnerships," Kutcher urges. "It's vital to our success—these private/public partnerships are the key."[332] He tirelessly advocates to make sure that Thorn has the strong links it needs so that they can develop robust and nimble ideas to launch into the real world.

Through promotional campaigns, educational programs, and other strategies, we can raise awareness of our technology across a broad spectrum of stakeholders. There are so many possible partners it's hard to know where to begin: hospitals, hotels, schools, churches, banks, restaurants, nail salons, libraries, gas stations, airports... the list goes on.

On the corporate level, Thorn saw an opportunity to catalyze the collaborative energies of huge software companies that are usually seen as rivals. "Microsoft and Facebook and Twitter and Google are competing every day in business," Kutcher says, "but they've all agreed to work together to find a solution to human trafficking and the sexual exploitation of children."[333] These companies have contributed to Thorn's work by subsidizing their employees to volunteer their time or by donating software packages to Thorn as well as other nonprofits. Human trafficking is an issue that brings them together.

---

332 Ibid.
333 "We are Thorn." *YouTube*, November 14, 2013. Thorn (September 28, 2019).

To that end, these companies have taken the initiative to eliminate criminal content on their own media platforms by participating in Thorn's shared hash program, which was adopted by the National Center for Missing and Exploited Children (NCMEC) in 2012. Thorn's executive director, Julie Cordua, explains how it works: "When one company finds a child abuse image on their network, they will report it to the national center, and they'll create a digital fingerprint of it and send it off to the cloud."[334] Through cloud storage, these companies can take advantage of much more data than they would have if they each monitored their own site in isolation. "All the other participating companies can pull that fingerprint down and find that image on *their* network," Cordua continues. "This results in more rapid identification and removal of this content across the Internet... and ideally will lead to quicker identification and rescue of these children."[335] Talk about life-changing collaboration!

And that's not all: in the past year, Thorn announced a new tool called Safer, aimed at equipping small or medium-sized companies to secure their sites against abusive content and child porn. "Larger companies have good systems in place but when you don't have the capacity to build out risks teams, then this type of bad content starts to flourish,"

---

334 Ibid.
335 Ibid.

Cordua says. "That's what we're trying to solve."[336] Companies like Imgur, Roblox, and Flickr are currently participating in a beta program to test out Safer's ability to weed out the content on their platforms. It's incredible to see companies across the industry establishing a network to identify and eradicate signs of human trafficking. It's not a competition—it's a team effort.

When I think about pursuing partnerships, Sherrie Caltagirone is another person who immediately pops into my mind. As the executive director of Global Emancipation Network, she spearheaded the development of a tool called Minerva, which aggregates and analyzes big data in order to extract meaningful information for stakeholders (See Chapter 4). And she's not about to stop, traveling around the globe to speak with potential donors, sponsors, and other partners, as well as potential customers. Her goal is to scale GEN's capacities to the international level by gaining access to data beyond the U.S. and Europe, so that Minerva can provide even more insight into trafficking networks that operate on a global level.

"We are completely reliant on our volunteers and the tech community at large, too," Sherrie says. In particular, Global Emancipation Network's entire toolset was donated by their partners, from the data analytics platform contributed by

---

336 Dickey, Megan Rose. "Why Google engineers worked full-time to combat sex trafficking." *TechCrunch*, January 15, 2019. Verizon Media (September 28, 2019).

Splunk to the Azure cloud computing services furnished by Microsoft. Without these products, the volunteers at GEN would not have been able to create Minerva so quickly, or so easily. Especially since GEN operates as a non-profit, Sherrie cannot stress enough how important it is to "really lean heavily on the corporate partners" who align with the anti-trafficking mission.[337]

Sherrie also hopes that GEN's work of bridging data silos will help break down the barriers to collaboration that keep other organizations, departments, and agencies from pooling their resources to work together on this mission. Whereas most agencies keep their data secluded in "silos" for security reasons, there's also so much potential in bringing separate stores of data together to reveal startling new discoveries. "We love to see the lightbulbs go off between the non-profit and the tech sector where we can help lead more non-profits to use data to improve their mission," Sherrie says.[338] Yes, it's a delicate task to prioritize privacy and respect other organizations' values, but facilitating cross-sectional trust is essential to eradicating slavery.

For their part, GEN's tech partners are incredibly supportive of the way that this non-profit organization embodies

---

337 Thorpe, Devin. "The New Sheriff In Human Trafficking Is Wielding Big Data." *Forbes*, October 11, 2018. Forbes Media (September 28, 2019).

338 "theCube Interview with Sherrie Caltagirone." *Global Emancipation NGO*, September 26, 2017. Global Emancipation Network (September 28, 2019).

the "Tech for Good" approach. "It is inspiring to see how a relatively small organization saw an opportunity to put their talents to work and went all in," says Justin Spelhaug, the manager of the Tech for Social Impact group within Microsoft Philanthropies. "GEN is just scratching the surface on the immense impact they can make in ending the human trafficking industry."[339]

And it's not just organization-level partnerships: Sherrie emphasizes the importance of teaming up as individuals, too. "I really appreciate the opportunities that I have and the ability I have to bring people onto our mission," she says, "and not only that but to really help open their eyes to the way that they can use their own interests and their skills... to do good in the world."[340] With this perspective, we can essentially partner with every citizen in the community by providing ways for them to contribute to the cause.

After all, any kind of partnership begins as the sharing of a vision, one person to another.

PERSEVERANCE

Even with the most optimal partnerships, obstacles are bound to arise. When times get tough, the ability to stay

339 Thorpe, Devin. "The New Sheriff In Human Trafficking Is Wielding Big Data." *Forbes*, October 11, 2018. Forbes Media (September 28, 2019).
340 Ibid.

resilient and flexible will be key in pushing through to bring an idea all the way to impact.

One example of a major setback is the federal shutdown of Backpage in April 2018, which threw both Thorn and Global Emancipation Network for a loop.[341] Backpage was a website that functioned as a major source of sex ads and thus, a major site for sex traffickers to profit off their victims. At first, it seems natural to close a website that circulates so much crime. However, although many heralded the shutdown as a success for anti-trafficking efforts, tech organizations like Thorn and GEN knew that it was only a game of whack-a-mole. They had been heavily relying on the Backpage website for scraping sex ads for data analysis; now, they had to regroup their efforts to scope out the smaller, scattered websites that the traffickers had moved to.

A month earlier, GEN had made their beta version of Minerva available for select customers to try out… but the shutdown hit them before they reached the MVP (minimum viable product) release. "One of our main sources of data was Backpage ads," volunteer Geoff Freeman told me. "A lot of the stuff we were collecting was straight from Backpage, and then the FBI came in and shut them down." Geoff said, "It was a major setback, because that was driving like eighty percent of the traffic. We were hamstrung in our capabilities

---

341 Jarrett, Laura and Sara Ashley O'Brien. "Justice Department seizes classified ads website Backpage.com." *CNN Politics*, April 6, 2018. CNN (September 28, 2019).

when that happened." They'd seen it coming, of course, but although Sherrie had shared her perspective in court, it hadn't been enough to prevent it.

It was a rough few months after that. "Basically, no new data was coming in until we were able to successfully onboard a new crawler," Geoff told me. The problem was that from one website to another, "when you're trying to grab things like age, and date of birth, or location, or the services that are offered, or the keywords," he explained, "you have to have a special script written for every different site, that knows how to pull [that information] out." However, they'd embedded the logic for extracting that information in the crawler code, and since it was Backpage-specific, they had to rework their entire crawler to make it compatible for other sites.

But they made it through. They were determined to bring their product all the way to the finish line, and they pulled it together—albeit with more late nights than they originally planned. Despite the obstacles they faced along the way, the team managed to meet their deadline and even exceeded expectations, celebrating the GA (general availability) release on September 24, 2018. Already, Minerva has been used to identify hundreds of thousands of victims, and over 989 individuals (including both traffickers and victims) have been referred to law enforcement action.

Like GEN, Thorn also had to redirect its momentum when Backpage shut down. "Once Backpage was gone, you were looking at an ecosystem in which all of those previously more centralized advertisements [for those being sex trafficked] are being redistributed," explained volunteer engineer Samantha Ainsley.[342] The advertisements that they'd been indexing from Backpage were now spread across a bunch of smaller sites.

Thankfully, Thorn's own employees weren't alone in working on this issue. In a groundbreaking partnership, Thorn was the first organization to participate in Google. org's new fellowship program, "which embeds Google engineers inside nonprofit organizations on a full-time basis for six months."[343] Sam Ainsley was one of these Google fellows who jumped on board as a Senior Software Engineer.

Ainsley said that the opportunity was just as vital for herself as it was for Thorn. "I had been at this crossroads in my career as an engineer, where I was feeling pretty siloed in terms of the impact that my work was having," Ainsley said in a TechCrunch interview. "I loved the work I was doing from a technical aspect—I always have—but I was considering potentially even exploring different career options because it was unclear to me how, through programming, I could have a direct impact on people's lives."[344] Working with Thorn has done just that, giving her a fresh new outlook on her place in the tech world.

---

342 Dickey, Megan Rose. "Why Google engineers worked full-time to combat sex trafficking." *TechCrunch*, January 15, 2019. Verizon Media (September 28, 2019).

343 Ibid.

344 Ibid.

For the Thorn team, the arrival of the five Google fellows couldn't have come at a more opportune time. The Google engineers dove into working with Thorn's staff to maximize the information that was still online and make it accessible to law enforcement. Since the traffickers' strategy was "to change things as quickly as possible to evade being found," a key objective for the engineers was to create profiles of victims out of seemingly unrelated information.[345] Then, officers "could actually understand that victim's history and where they might be at any given period of time," Ainsley said. "What are the cities they've been in over time? What are the various phone numbers they've used over time? How has their appearance changed?"[346]

Using their expertise in machine learning, the engineers were able to take "a holistic approach," which extracted an individual's history from an overwhelming number of ads—a task that would be daunting, if not impossible, for an actual person to undertake.[347] Ainsley used her data visualization skills to present that information to law enforcement in a way that was user-friendly and tailored to their needs. "We're really optimistic about where this can go," she said, adding that even though her six-month stint is officially over, she plans to keep up a weekly commitment with the Thorn team in order to see their

345 Ibid.
346 Ibid.
347 Ibid.

prototype launch into action. "I want to be available as much as I possibly can to assist in that effort," she said.[348] This relationship between Google and Thorn is a remarkable example of engineers coming together to accomplish more than they could have done alone, enabling them to persevere despite setbacks.

The Backpage shutdown didn't just create upheaval for organizations like Thorn and Global Emancipation Network that developed technology to aid anti-trafficking efforts. Victim service providers also felt its effects, especially organizations like Real Escape from the Sex Trade (REST) in Seattle, which had been piloting an outreach text platform to contact potential victims who were advertised online. The technology was taking off, giving the REST staff excitement that they could now offer support to victims who were otherwise unreachable.

However, the removal of Backpage meant that many victims no longer had an online presence. Jackie Loos, who became REST's Outreach Coordinator in January 2018, witnessed an unprecedented shift from online ad-based sex trafficking to on-street trafficking. "I stood out there for about ten minutes one night, and I was able to watch four or five girls get into buyers' cars," Jackie remembers.[349] "Suddenly,

---

348 Ibid.
349 "When They Go Back to the Streets, So Do We." *I Want Rest Blog*, October 23, 2018. Real Escape from the Sex Trade (September 28, 2019).

our texts weren't reaching victims—and there was a resurgence in street trafficking." In charge of implementing crisis response, Jackie knew she had to rethink REST's tactics as quickly as possible.

Pivoting quickly, Jackie relaunched REST's street outreach team, comprised of red-jacketed individuals who are trained to interact with victims tactfully and consistently (and quickly, because pimps are usually present) to reach these sex workers who appeared on the streets of Seattle at night. While she still manages REST's automatic text outreach, Jackie recognizes that the technology is only one piece of their strategy. Ultimately, the goal of REST's outreach team is to "[let] them know who we are and what we do," she told me, and they'll use whatever will be the most effective means to accomplish that goal.

It's inspiring to see how Thorn, Global Emancipation Network, and REST all found ways to be resilient as the landscape of sex trafficking changed during the spring of April 2018—this kind of flexibility will help any organization overcome whatever hurdles come in their way.

PROMISE

At the end of it all is a splash of hope.

It's the little victories, the milestones that we can celebrate: "We've taken these investigation times of dark web material from three years down to what we believe to be three weeks," Kutcher shared in Congress in 2017.[350] Someday, he hopes that anti-trafficking investigations will be so agile in extinguishing online exploitation that they practically won't be needed at all.

It's the thrill of having a weapon that wields real power. As Sherrie says, it's "really promising that the very technologies traffickers are using... is the very same technologies that we can use against them to combat trafficking."[351] Giving them a taste of their own medicine, if you will. She is confident that with technology on our side, eventually, justice will prevail.

And it's the vision of what the future could be like: "Every single story I hear about a child being identified and assisted makes my heart sing," software engineer Chase Ricketts wrote after working at Thorn for one month.[352] This is the long-term perspective: children playing without fear, women and girls treated with respect, workers actually receiving the wages they rightfully earn. A freedom-filled world—that's our horizon.

These promises ultimately energize the software engineers working on the code itself and leaders like Ashton

350 "Ashton Kutcher Speech on Human Trafficking Before Congress." *YouTube*, February 15, 2017. ABC News (September 28, 2019).

351 Magee, Tamlin. "Inside GEN, the nonprofit combatting human trafficking with big data." *Computerworld*, January 11, 2019. IDG Communications (September 28, 2019).

352 Ricketts, Chase. "My First 30 Days as a Software Engineer at Thorn." *Thorn Blog*, October 11, 2016. Thorn (September 28, 2019).

Kutcher and Sherrie Caltagirone to keep on transforming their mission into a reality.

When you can push through to deliver a project that takes strides toward a world without slavery?

It's one hundred percent worth it.

CHAPTER 10:

PERSONAL CHALLENGES

"I anticipated learning some dark things about the world, but I didn't know how deep the rabbit hole went."

—CHASE RICKETTS, SOFTWARE ENGINEER AT THORN[353]

Developing technological solutions against human trafficking is not merely a mental challenge—it's logistically taxing and emotionally exhausting as well. In this chapter, you'll get a glimpse into the day-in, day-out grittiness that these individuals experience, from financial limitations to inflated expectations to secondhand trauma.

This is a reality that I've wrestled with as I consider whether I'm "cut out" for this kind of work. The last thing

---

353 Ricketts, Chase. "My First 30 Days as a Software Engineer at Thorn." *Thorn Blog*, October 11, 2016. Thorn (September 28, 2019).

I want is to jump in, itching to make a difference, only to tumble out of the space a few months later, burnt out and disillusioned. Listening to the stories of technologists who've come to terms with their own struggles, I've realized that it will always be hard. However, through seeking out support, keeping the end in sight, and channeling distressing situations into productive directions, they've found the strength to keep on.

ONLY SO MUCH TIME

One of the most obvious limitations on a technologists' work in the anti-trafficking space is simply time. Often, these individuals are software engineers who volunteer their hours outside of work. After spending a full day debugging code, pitching projects, and sitting through meetings, they choose to spend their free time writing yet more software for organizations that wouldn't have been able to do it without their help. Truly, kudos to these tech volunteers!

However, donated hours have their drawbacks. When I chatted with Liz Rush, the anti-trafficking technology director at Seattle Against Slavery, she shared what it's like for her to coordinate volunteers as they build SAS's Freedom Signal platform. "Volunteers are so challenging," she told me. "You can't have deadlines in the same way as employees, which makes planning really difficult... You can't expect people to be on-call for a volunteer job." Needless to say, coordinating schedules and deadlines can be a hassle.

I then had the chance to hear from a tech volunteer himself: Geoff Freeman, a senior software engineer at Microsoft who formerly volunteered for the non-profit organization called Global Emancipation Network. He kindly agreed to share his perspective with me. "I wasn't able to do as much work with GEN as I'd hoped," he admitted, although his co-worker Emilia assured me that he played a crucial role in structuring the ingestion pipeline.

When I talked with him, Geoff gave a brief backstory leading up to his work with GEN. "I kind of got a sideways entry into the tech world," he said, explaining that he'd never finished college before entering the tech industry. Thus, while currently working full-time at Microsoft, he was also taking one course per term to complete his computer science degree in the next three to four years.

Despite these dual demands on his time, human trafficking was an issue that he deeply cared about. He didn't have any firsthand experience, but he'd read articles about the crime and knew it was a horrible injustice that he would be eager to help eradicate. Around 2017, he remembers, "I got introduced to Sherrie at Global Emancipation Network through a friend that I went to high school with, named Corey Marshall," who worked for a software company called Splunk. As director of their "Splunk for Good" social impact initiative, Marshall partnered closely with GEN to help them utilize Splunk's software for big data analysis.

Geoff decided to volunteer his time to help GEN out where he could. "I came in and I helped them with building out parts of their scraper and ingestion pipeline," he explained. "By far, the most that I did was just help them with design architecture and building out what next generations of their system could look like." He wanted to make sure that their ingestion pipeline would be able to scale well when onboarding new scraper sources; in other words, making it easier to collect, aggregate, and analyze data from any online source that might contain information relevant to human trafficking. "One of the things that I helped to do was investigate different options that would help [GEN] scale their scraper and also make it more maintainable and extensible," Geoff said.

He added, "The other place where GEN needed some work was what their data analysis and ingestion pipeline look like." When he first joined their technical team, the data was lumped into what is called a "blob store," which made it difficult to perform useful operations on it. "I was helping them convert that to something [with more structure] where they would be able to use [query languages] like newSQL to do bigger analysis on it."

During the upheaval triggered by the shutdown of Backpage.com—when GEN had to quickly implement new code to extract data from less familiar websites—Geoff felt like he couldn't keep up with all the changes that were happening with Minerva. As the team pushed to get the MVP release ready, "the code was churning more and more, and I was getting more and more out of touch with what was in the code, which makes you less and less effective as a developer," he told me.

"I was hoping to help more with the implementation, [but] it was changing so rapidly," Geoff said. He didn't have the time to fully engage with each update, which prevented him from offering much help to the team. "Between work and school," he remembered, "I was able to devote maybe five hours a week to GEN, and that was enough for me to get in the way." The last thing he wanted was to hold the others back as they struggled to keep him up-to-task while also pushing ahead toward the MVP release of Minerva.

I could sense his frustration. If only he'd had more time to commit, he would have gladly done all he could to contribute to GEN's work. It wasn't a lack of passion; there simply weren't enough hours in the day. And since his involvement with Global Emancipation Network was only a volunteer project, Geoff reluctantly allowed his schoolwork and full-time job to take higher priority.

"I ended up working with [GEN] until about a month before the MVP release," he remembers. Then, he told them he had to "'step away" for a while. While Geoff sounded disappointed that he couldn't contribute more, I admire him for doing what he thought would improve the overall performance of the GEN team. Even though he never personally got to see "the immediate impact of [Minerva] and the way that it is improving people's lives," he never lost sight of the greater goal.

I asked him, "After you finish school, would you like to get back into this type of volunteer tech work in the future?" Geoff didn't hesitate. "Absolutely!"

His graduation is about four years out, but he says there's a good chance he'll be resuming anti-trafficking work in some way in the future. "I think [fighting] human trafficking is incredibly important," he told me. "It's [an issue] that I feel pretty passionate about, that I would like to give back towards."

I'm sure he will.

FAMILY COMES FIRST

Apart from limitations on time, personal priorities can also hamper technologists' ability to commit to anti-trafficking efforts. For example, Emilia Vanderwerf gradually found it difficult to juggle her family's stability and her work with Global Emancipation Network. When I reached out to her, she thoughtfully agreed to share some of her story with me.

It was 2016. Emilia had left her software engineer position at Dell after her first daughter was born, embracing her new job as a stay-at-home mom. Reading and gardening and playing with her kids were wonderful, of course, but after about a year, she was ready for something more. "I was staying at home with my kids at the time and was looking for both an intellectual outlet that would contribute positively to my career as a software engineer, and I was looking for a way to contribute positively to a team," she told me. She missed the excitement of tackling challenges that reached beyond her own little world.

It was time to put her technical skills back to work.

That's when Christine Chen called. Emilia had met Christine at the University of Portland years back when Christine was a freshman and Emilia was in her last year. "Emilia is a such a kind, wise friend and mentor," Christine told me. They'd connected not only over computer science but also their pursuit of intellectual excellence and a desire to use their skills for social good. Now a senior in the fall of 2016, Christine was in the process of applying to graduate school. She remembers that she asked Emilia to look over "my personal statement in which I mentioned the work I was doing with GEN," an incredible nonprofit that was just getting off the ground. Intrigued, Emilia asked her about it over Skype.

According to Christine, Sherrie Caltagirone had presented about Global Emancipation Network during a visit to the University of Portland (her husband Sergio's alma mater). Christine had jumped on board to help with one of their tech projects, and other computer science students had started planning their senior capstone project with GEN to generate an international online directory of VSPs (victim service providers). The door was wide open: Sherrie was looking for people who could donate their time and skills toward

GEN's mission… and Emilia had both. "The timing ended up being perfect," she told me.

Soon afterward, Emilia reached out to Sherrie and began spending ten to twenty hours a week volunteering for Global Emancipation Network. She took charge of the technical side of Minerva, facilitating coordination among the tech volunteers as they worked remotely to design a system that would be able to ingest vast online datasets, which would, in turn, provide insight into trafficking activity. The volunteers then "analyzed the text and image data for geographic information, personal identification, and similarity using natural language processing, hashing, and computer vision [techniques]."

Emilia loved being able to do something good for the world while still staying at home with her daughters. It was the best of both worlds, a rare alignment of passion and priority. However, this alignment began to dissolve about a year later, when Emilia began looking for full-time work again. Volunteering part-time wasn't realistic if she wanted to provide for her family. She thought she might have to step back from her work with GEN.

Thankfully, Emilia didn't have to choose. Through providential timing, GEN received a generous dose of support from the Loyola Foundation—president Andrea Hattler Bramson had discerned potential in the anti-trafficking NGO and decided to include GEN in a special fund to commemorate her foundation's 60th anniversary. "I truly have her to thank!" Emilia told me. That donation was used to directly fund a new position for a lead full-stack software engineer, which she happily filled.

Her family readjusted as Emilia became the primary breadwinner and her husband quit his job to become a stay-at-home dad. "As I transitioned into a full-time role [with GEN], I had the opportunity to be the Scrum Master," Emilia explained, which meant that she led the weekly volunteer meetings, managed the team to maximize their agility and productivity, and planned the dates for Minerva's GA (General Availability) release. "I also helped determine which features would be most valuable to customers... [and estimate] whether they would be able to fit into our timeline. It was fun to wear a lot of hats!" In many ways, it was the best job in the world.

Nevertheless, Emilia's position was always shadowed by uncertainty, which is to be expected in any non-profit that depends on funding from outside donors. It would be a "very privileged situation," Emilia explained, to be able to "meld stability and tech for good." Sherrie is working tirelessly to raise the next round of funds for Global Emancipation Network's future projects. Until then, it's a delicate balance to bring in enough income to support a family while devoting the skills and time toward anti-trafficking work.

Emilia is proud to have done her part in bringing GEN closer to having a product that will draw paying customers. She was present for Minerva's MVP release and then for the GA release, which exceeded expectations despite the setbacks they'd faced along the way. As she shared these milestones with me over the phone, she lingered deliberately over the date: September 24, 2018. It was a bittersweet moment for her because while it marked a huge success, it was also her "last day" as a hands-on developer at GEN.

Except for integrating customer feedback to optimize Minerva's search architecture, tech development came to a halt after the GA release because the volunteers had basically finished their project. Now, with Minerva released to public customers, GEN is in the regrouping phase, gathering the resources they need to tackle their next endeavor. Sherrie has been busy raising funds and trying to gain access to more data internationally while Emilia has been helping out with customer calls as well as advising the next group of volunteers.

When I called her over the phone, Emilia was just about to start a new job at a "regular" tech company. Family stability is a priority, she explained, although she still helps Sherrie out when she can. Although it must have been a difficult choice, I think she's right: you can't make the world a better place if you don't take care of your own small sphere first.

"In the future, once my husband goes back to work and the kids go to school, I'd love to get back into humanitarian tech work," Emilia told me. Her motivation is boundless. Whether it's combating human trafficking or addressing another critical current issue, she knows she'll find a way to use her skills for good in the world.

NOT ALWAYS GLAMOROUS

Another challenge that technologists face is that anti-trafficking tech work is often not nearly as glamorous nor as straightforward as they thought. That's something that I learned from my friend Christine, as she's graciously welcomed me into her journey.

In June 2018, after I mentioned in my end-of-term honors reflection that I was interested in exploring ways to develop technology for anti-trafficking work, my professor Dr. Kirsten Foot offered to connect me with a computer science graduate student who'd just finished her first year at the University of Washington. According to Dr. Foot, Christine Chen had volunteered and interned with several different anti-trafficking organizations.

Really? I was super excited to meet Christine and learn from her experience.

We met that summer at a cafe near campus. Over coffee, we chatted about our mutual passion to do something in the fight against slavery, our desire to channel the power of technology in this space, and our struggle to know how to contribute most effectively. Since then, Christine has become such an amazing, encouraging friend.

Before her senior year of college, Christine knew very little about modern-day slavery. "My sister got a dress at a shop where all proceeds were donated to combat sex trafficking," she remembers, but that was about it. Distant and dim. It wasn't something she thought about. She was majoring in computer science, so why would human trafficking be on her radar?

All that changed one autumn day when Sherrie Caltagirone, the executive director of Global Emancipation Network, visited Christine's computer science club at the University of Portland, Oregon. It was a wake-up call unlike anything Christine had ever experienced. "As Sherrie shared about the realities of human trafficking, the ways that technology can be used to facilitate trafficking, and the ways that her organization uses technology to fight against trafficking, I felt compelled to join," she told me. "I don't think I've ever had a stronger sense of the rightness of a decision or made a decision so quickly in my life."

As soon as the talk was over, Christine went up to Sherrie and asked if she could get involved. "Sure!" Sherrie responded. In fact, she could help them "research ways to automate the process of creating a database of anti-trafficking organizations"—that's how Christine described it to me. The problem was providing a way for victims, survivors, and service providers to find the resources that they needed. While some databases did exist, they weren't very useful in connecting people to organizations. "They tend to be sparsely populated because organizations must learn about the database in the first place and then apply to enter," Christine told me. What if, instead, a program could automatically find and add the organizations without making them do any extra work?

With the help of her undergraduate research adviser and GEN's technical director Sergio, Christine spent her senior year on a project to streamline that process of creating a comprehensive online directory. "I built a prototype consisting of two major modules," she explained. First, she developed a "discovery module that collects anti-trafficking organization websites based on Twitter data mining." The second piece was a "scraping module that utilizes natural language processing techniques to extract key information from those websites (e.g. address, phone number, social media presence, etc.)" Applying the tools of data mining and natural language processing, she helped GEN gather information about many more organizations than they could have found by scrolling online manually.

It was Christine's first exposure to the exciting applications of technology in the anti-trafficking community, but it certainly wouldn't be her last. From there, she was hooked. She and her research adviser brainstormed future projects for GEN with Sherrie and "pitched [them] to the juniors as potential senior projects," encouraging continued collaboration between University of Portland students and Global Emancipation Network even after she had left. "When I graduated," she recalled, "two senior design teams had decided to work on GEN projects" for their capstone.

In fact, computer science students Melanie Martinell, Michelle Lau, and Nick Accuardi picked up where Christine had left off on her own project. "We learn how to code, but how do we apply that knowledge to helping people?" says Nick, reflecting on his experience.[354] Working on the directory provided just that opportunity to do meaningful tech work. In fact, Sergio believed that this directory of anti-trafficking organizations would be "a one-of-a-kind technology tool which will help millions," enabling stakeholders like law enforcement and victim service providers to find each other, communicate, and develop partnerships for more effective efforts.[355]

Christine herself, though, had to find a new direction to pursue after graduation. She already planned to work toward a PhD at the University of Washington, but she "was eager to gain more experience in the anti-trafficking/nonprofit space before grad school." The good thing was that after working on the database for GEN, she was familiar with many of the anti-trafficking organizations out there. In particular, one that kept "popping up time and time again in the list" was International Justice Mission (IJM), a faith-based, nongovernmental organization dedicated to ending slavery by working with local police authorities to rescue and rehabilitate victims, as well as discouraging traffickers through more stringent enforcement of the justice system. "That piqued my curiosity," Christine said. Interning at the headquarters

---

354 "Engineering students work with Global Emancipation Network on coding project." *UP News*, March 14, 2018. University of Portland (September 28, 2019).

355 Ibid.

of a well-established anti-slavery organization, with a global team of lawyers, social workers, and investigators in seventeen field offices around the world, would be a dream come true. While exploring IJM's website, she found that they had a technology internship and decided to apply. It felt like "a shot in the dark… but it couldn't hurt to try."

Soon afterward, she was packing her bags for a summer in Washington, D.C.

Christine couldn't wait to make an impact during her few months with IJM. She told me that she was expecting to write "commands to analyze and alert on incoming data from firewalls and routers," similar to research she'd done in college when she analyzed system metadata to detect potential system threats.[356] By designing alerts based off of incoming data, she'd be able to help IJM maximize the usefulness of their security information and events management tool. It was exciting, it was powerful, and it would allow her to put her technical skills to work.

However, as they "poked around with the existing tool," it wasn't long before it became clear that Christine shouldn't spend her time building off of that framework with data analysis. Instead, she found that the tool itself wasn't the best fit. She needed to look for a completely different security tool that would serve IJM better. So rather than spending

---

356 "STEM Education and Outreach Center Newsletter, Winter 2017 Edition." *UP STEM*, February 21, 2015. University of Portland (September 28, 2019).

two months writing code that engaged her technical skills, Christine spent her internship making a lot of phone calls, researching the market for other tools to replace the current one. Phone calls are just one of the aspects of any tech development project that are critical but extremely tedious. Beyond market research, a software engineer often must test their code rigorously, refactor it to optimize performance, clean it up and document it thoroughly so that it is neat, elegant, and easy for another programmer to pick up where it was left off, if needed. For data scientists, it can be boring to make sure that all the data is in the correct format in order to be useful; for user experience designers, their user research protocol can sometimes seem more like a formality than an informative process. Especially for these technologists who want to *see* their impact working against human trafficking, these invisible tasks can seem very uninspiring. Remember tech ego? Oftentimes, discarding that desire to be the "hero" means redefining your expectations of what impact really looks like.

Christine found that out through personal experience. If there ever was a test of her true passion, this was it. She had "really wanted to do technical work!" Yet when her years of computer science knowledge seemed useless, Christine had to ask herself whether she was ultimately willing to support the anti-trafficking cause regardless of whether it required her technical skills or not. It was a major challenge, she told me, "completely letting go of my idea of what would be the most fulfilling/interesting... and embracing my role as doing whatever would best support the team and mission." In the end, she was able to help her team "pivot to a more effective solution," coming away with the realization that technical know-how alone cannot solve every problem.

This dizzying, humbling perspective grew stronger when Christine started graduate school to pursue a PhD in computer science at the University of Washington. Naturally, she wanted to conduct research that would be relevant to anti-trafficking work, so she spent her first year interviewing survivors, advocates, and other staff members of victim service provider (VSP) organizations for both labor and sex trafficking, mostly based in urban areas of the United States. "My goal," she recalls, "was to understand how [VSP staff members] use technology as they interact with survivors and what their computer security and privacy concerns are with this technology usage." She was hoping that the information she found would give her an idea of how to develop some sort of technology that could help address the primary concerns of these VSPs.

The answer certainly wasn't clear-cut. Rather, it further increased her understanding that it is naive to treat technology as the definitive solution. It's impossible to solve human trafficking with just one more software platform. Instead, her findings highlighted "the need for members of the computer security and privacy community to work with VSPs to develop solutions and/or provide education to help strike the right balance" when it comes to technology interventions.[357] But when it comes to a plan that she can take action on? She's still trying to figure that out.

"I came away rather overwhelmed by all the other factors… that make recovery so difficult and revictimization so easy," Christine told me. "Yes, technology is important, but it is also just one piece of the puzzle especially when thinking about the victims and survivors. There is poverty, homelessness, drugs, trauma, immigration, and so many other pieces. And I believe that all those pieces need to inform the technology piece. But how do I understand those other pieces more fully as a computer scientist?"

For her, "The path forward lies in collaborating more closely with organizations on the ground." That's why she continues to participate in anti-trafficking events and fundraisers throughout the year. She's also joined the UW Police Department's cadet program to learn more about law enforcement and brainstorm ways for them to build bridges with vulnerable populations. As far as the technology side goes, she admitted that she doesn't know yet where she wants to focus her efforts, but she's hopeful that getting experience outside of the tech world will inform her understanding of

---

357 Chen et al. "Computer Security and Privacy in the Interactions Between Victim Service Providers and Human Trafficking Survivors." *28th USENIX Security Symposium*, 2019. USENIX (September 28, 2019).

what needs to be done… so that when she sees a need that technology can fill, she'll be ready.

IT TAKES ITS TOLL

While it's deeply fulfilling to develop cutting-edge technology that will help eradicate human trafficking, this kind of work also takes its heavy toll.

For instance, when I asked Geoff Freeman if it was easy to get lost in the code and forget about the people on the other side of it, he paused for a long moment. "The work that I was doing… I don't think it's *possible* to lose sight of [the larger issue that you're working against]," he answered. "On the one hand, you're working on these datasets, trying to find [new patterns], and every time you look at some test data, you're always like, *oh my! oh! Oh, that's*— it's, it's right in your face. And I kept expecting to get desensitized to it, and I don't think I ever really did."

Even if technologists aren't directly interacting with survivors on a daily basis, being in the anti-slavery space— living and breathing with that issue weighing heavy in the air—is hard, psychologically and emotionally, like Geoff described. Formally, this is known as vicarious trauma, which the American Counseling Association describes as the "emotional residue of exposure" to stories of pain, terror, and abuse.[358] When someone suffers from vicarious trauma,

---

358 "Vicarious Trauma." *Counseling Fact Sheets*, 2019. American Counseling Association (September 28, 2019).

they can feel exhausted, trapped, hopeless, dissatisfied, or withdrawn… among a host of symptoms.

Sometimes, it can even be paralyzing.

Liz Rush found this out the hard way about a year into her job as technology director at Seattle Against Slavery. When I talked with her, she shared a story that was still fresh in her memory. "Recently one of our partner organizations sent us a copy of a journal that a woman had left lying at a hotel," she began. In the pages, she'd written about how she was being exploited for sex, advertised online, and how she wasn't allowed to keep her money. But it wasn't just the details of exploitation that sent Liz spiraling.

"The thing that hit me was that it was written in pink and purple gel pens, with really girly handwriting," she remembers. "To see it in handwriting versus what you see online…" After working for months in front of a screen, Liz was shaken by how personal and *real* this victim was—it wasn't merely an entry in a database. And the only trace they had of her was this notebook, whispering of horrors she was still enduring.

"I couldn't get it out of my head for two weeks," Liz said. "I'd sit down and try to program, and even though I know that the code that I'm working on is going to help reduce exploitation, you can't really focus on your code syntax or bug fixing or whatever when *that* is also in your head."

Curlicues in purple ink, a haunting cry for help.

It led to "a pretty serious bout of burnout for about a month," Liz remembered. "I felt like I wasn't being pro-

ductive, wasn't coding enough, wasn't getting enough done…
One day it just made me tear up on my lunch break—I can't
be here right now."

When it becomes detrimental to your ability to concentrate and contribute effectively, it's okay to take a break.
When I talked with Justin Underwood, he agreed that stepping back is something you'll have to do from time to time.
As an intelligence analyst who has volunteered his time with
Global Emancipation Network, he's faced similar vicarious
trauma from being steeped in the sex trafficking space. "You
got to maintain your mental health," he said, "because you
are dealing with some of the ugliest things in society."

For him, it's not just the injustice of one person exploiting another that disturbs him, while that on its own is
heartbreaking—it's also the fact that so many "good" people
in the world aren't doing anything to combat the problem.
Not only that, "there are powerful people who are benefiting
from the human trafficking network and conducting and
contributing" to it. These are people in law enforcement,
people with money and influence, politicians… That's really
what infuriates him more than anything. "When you run
into things like that, it is not only a professional frustration,
it is a personal frustration," he told me. "That really, really
angers me to my core." It's exhausting to feel like you're
one of a very small set of people who are trying to live in
integrity, when the people in power are getting away with
blatant injustice.

Another burden, Justin said, is the psychological toll of his work. Sometimes he's able to contribute to combating trafficking from a more removed standpoint, but when he is directly involved in an investigation, such as looking at forums on the dark web, it's hard not to be affected by the content he sees. "It's disgusting. People are openly discussing... talking about, for example, a child [sex trafficking victim] and their experiences with him and speaking about them as either they're a resource or if they're actually, I mean, *asking* for it." Blaming the victim is an excuse that's been used way too long—it's nauseating. As a human intelligence collector and intelligence analyst, his job is to "get into their minds to be able to understand how they operate, how I can exploit their supply chain." He knows that by doing this work he'll be able to disrupt what they're doing, but he definitely doesn't enjoy the task.

And yet, there are details that you can't talk about or process with other people, especially when working as an intelligence professional, as Justin was. Based on his personal experience and from what he's seen in other people, he's seen that "it makes people jaded." He's curious how long people last in the anti-trafficking sector, noting, "I can only imagine the burnout rate is extremely high." I don't think anyone's keeping numbers on this, but Justin's point made me wonder about it, too.

It's gotten so upsetting for him that Justin said there have been "times where I've taken a step back for six months, and just don't even look into it." Thankfully, though, he has the support he needs to keep going and rebound even after months of burnout. "My wife has been extremely supportive and understanding of the type of work I do," he said. She notices when his sleep patterns are interrupted or other bad habits start popping up and helps him stay self-aware as to when he needs to take a break.

Support from like-minded coworkers is also tremendously valuable when wrestling with vicarious trauma. For one, Liz Rush is grateful that at Seattle Against Slavery, she's part of a team who've experienced similar feelings and can understand her psychological state. In the tech world, "you have to be productive to be valuable," she says, but at SAS, "there's no shame or guilt attached to it." When she was struggling through her period of burnout, her coworkers were there for her… because at some time or other, they've all experienced that secondary trauma.

She's learned how to be open about it, too. For instance, she'll acknowledge when "I'm really feeling this right now." It's important to take a break and talk through things before it becomes problematic. At the same time, Liz says that she'll be able to "channel those feelings into my work" in order to make strides toward preventing those stories of exploitation from happening in the future. As difficult as it is, she doesn't want to lose the raw passion that initially drew her into this space—because that is what ultimately motivates her to pursue this mission.

Phil Bennett agrees. While he's careful not to let himself burn out, he actually wouldn't want to lose that emotion that he felt when he was on the ground meeting sex trafficking survivors in India for the first time. "I don't want to treat it like another job," he told me. "I want to do something that I'm passionate about now." It's work that you have to be deeply, personally invested in—it comes with its emotional toll, but that internal fire is what makes it worth doing in the first place.

That's why Justin Underwood chose to return to anti-trafficking work after his six-month hiatus. In fact, the source of his frustration is what keeps him committed to this space: "So many people know, but so few people talk about it, and even less people actually do something that makes a difference." If he stepped away for good, he'd become exactly who he doesn't want to be.

No matter how paralyzing it can be to work on such tough issues, no matter how upsetting to remember the real individuals behind the data, no matter how overwhelming to consider how much still needs to be done, he's going to be one of those few people taking action.

Hopefully, his example—and that of Geoff, Emilia, Liz, and Christine—will inspire others to take a stand as well.

CHAPTER 11:

FOR A FUTURE OF FREEDOM

———

"Whether [it's] technology for businesses to map their supply chains, or an app for everyone to have in their pocket…this isn't just a gimmick, it's an essential part of the fight to eradicate slavery."

—ANDREW WALLIS, CEO OF UNSEEN UK[359]

When I sat in the cafeteria in February 2018, adding an honors course about human trafficking to my registration plan, I couldn't imagine the journey that awaited me.

———

359 "Unseen Launches App to Report Modern Slavery." *Unseen News,* July 30, 2018. Unseen UK (September 28, 2019).

I knew that hearing stories from victims around the world would be unsettling, but I didn't realize it would convict me of my own indifference and call me into a mission that reached far beyond my small sphere. A mission for justice, restoration, and freedom.

Ever since then, I couldn't turn back.

TRAIL BLAZERS

When my friend Christine Chen told me about her experience volunteering with Global Emancipation Network (GEN), she offered to connect me with Sherrie, GEN's executive director, to see how I could get involved. Starry-eyed and eager to jump in, I immediately agreed.

Amidst her busy schedule, Sherrie somehow found time to call me while sitting in her car one autumn afternoon; on the other end of the phone, I paced my dorm room with a mixture of nervousness, excitement, and intimidation. I wanted so badly to get started right away as a volunteer—this felt more stressful than the technical interviews my friends warned me about.

I worked up the courage over the course of our conversation, finally blurting, "If there's *any* way I can help out, I'd love to contribute to GEN's work."

But I could already sense what her answer was going to be.

"I appreciate your passion," Sherrie told me [paraphrased]. "And I encourage people who want to support this cause, to find ways to be involved… but at the same time, we have to be mindful that anyone who joins our team is going to be an asset."

I took another lap around my room, feeling my inadequacy engulf me. "Yes... that makes sense. I definitely wouldn't want to be a burden."

Although she was tactful enough not to say it aloud, Sherrie knew that I probably wouldn't have been much help to GEN at the time. I had to admit, she was right. I'd only taken one year of computer science courses, after all. I had no idea what it meant to "scrape" phone numbers off a website, or how to query a database—or even how the Internet worked. While I was enthralled by the possibilities of big data analysis, I had a long way to go before I could truly be useful in a technical capacity.

Still, Sherrie knew that I was trying to find my footing in the space, so she gave me a firehose of information. It was all I could do to keep up with her, scribbling down the names of organizations that were utilizing tech tools to combat human trafficking.

Our conversation left me dazed, with the overwhelming realization that I had so much to learn if I wanted to be a part of the tech-for-anti-trafficking space. At the same time, I also came away with a more concrete direction to pursue. Something to work toward, something to spur me on.

From that phone call, I embarked on a journey to scope out a world I never knew existed.

I had thought I was the only one interested in using technology to fight human trafficking, but I couldn't have been more wrong. Over the next several months, as I became acquainted with tech volunteers from GEN and elsewhere, I found so many role models to emulate: individuals like Liz, Phil, Emilia, Geoff, and Justin.

I couldn't have guessed that I would discover an entire community of technologists who've accepted the challenge to take on modern-day slavery. In an age where many enter the tech industry for its self-serving benefits, these individuals go out of their way to support a cause that they deeply care about, seeking to contribute their skills in an area that is critically devoid of cutting-edge technology.

From web developers to data analysts to software engineers, they see where they're needed, and they say, "I'm here to help." With creativity and humility, they're tackling a formidable problem and kindle impact all around: analyzing the movements of perpetrators; deterring buyers of trafficked goods and services; increasing supply chain transparency; designing tools for law enforcement; reaching out to potential victims; providing ways for the community to get involved; and empowering survivors to seize the power of technology for themselves.

They are the humblest trailblazers. In order to do what they do, these technologists have to sacrifice their hours, often on top of a full-time job. Sometimes they give up a more lucrative paycheck. They have to be willing to learn from other stakeholders in the anti-trafficking space and admit that they usually aren't the experts. And they open themselves up to the emotional burden of dealing with an issue that involves real people trapped in horrible situations by their fellow human beings. Together, they're making strides toward eradicating modern-day slavery.

I see myself echoed in each of their stories, which inspires me to press forward with the heart, humility, and hope that they exemplify so well.

It would be the greatest honor to join them.

ONLY THE BEGINNING

When it comes to combating human trafficking, I truly believe that we're on the brink of transforming technology into a real force to be reckoned with. We're initiating more conversations than ever about the need for anti-slavery actors to team up with tech partners, and the momentum is growing. It's not change *yet*, but discussion is the first step toward action.

For example, a coalition called **Tech Against Trafficking** was formed in June 2018, arising out of a "strong willingness to collaborate" between the United Nations, civil society organizations, and global tech companies such as BT, Salesforce, and Microsoft.[360] These entities recognized that if they came together, they could capitalize

---

360 Nestor, Peter, Dunstan Allison-Hope, and Hannah Darnton. "Announcing a New Collaboration Using Tech to Combat Human

on "real opportunities to make an impact."[361] As a first project, they undertook the compilation of a list of more than 200 tech tools currently used in anti-trafficking work, mapping the current landscape in order to determine best steps moving forward. In this book, I've described about ten of these tools—that's only five percent of what's currently out there!

Now, the Tech Against Trafficking coalition is in the process of developing ideas for various mobile apps to address the needs of "first-line responders, the public, and vulnerable workers."[362] They're making plans to bring laptops and smartphones—hardware that seems commonplace to us—to victim service provider organizations who directly support vulnerable individuals. They're designing systems to enhance supply chain transparency to prevent labor trafficking, as well as national helplines to improve responses. Lastly, they're working on methods of handling data so that stakeholders can pick out patterns that they wouldn't have otherwise noticed, which in turn enhances their responses to urgent situations.

There's also **Delta 8.**7, a global knowledge platform created by the United Nations University Centre for Policy Research as a direct contribution toward the UN's

Trafficking." *BSR*, June 28, 2018. Business for Social Responsibility (September 28, 2019).
361 Ibid.
362 Ibid.

Sustainable Development Goals for 2030, in which "193 countries pledged their commitment to take effective measures to eradicate modern slavery, human trafficking, forced labour and child labour."[363] Through research, visualization of measurements in data dashboards, and promoting dialogue at their co-hosted Code 8.7 conference and symposiums, Delta 8.7 helps extract meaningful conclusions from data to inform policymakers and other stakeholders seeking to collaborate most effectively.

Then there's **Liberty Shared**, a nongovernmental organization focused on preventing human trafficking "through legal advocacy, technological interventions, and strategic collaborations with NGOs & corporations globally."[364] Their projects include the Freedom Collaborative, an online platform for sharing information among stakeholders so that they can "increase their collaborative capacity," as well as an Information and Data Collaboration program, which collects publicly available information and turns it into interactive dashboards and visualizations that stakeholders can use as they make decisions.[365]

363 "What is Delta 8.7?." *Delta 8.7*, 2019. United Nations University Centre for Policy Research to Alliance 8.7 (September 28, 2019).

364 "Liberty Shared: Creating an Environment Safe from Trafficking." *Liberty Shared*, 2019. Share (Asia Pacific) Limited (September 28, 2019).

365 "Freedom Collaborative." *Liberty Shared*, 2019. Share (Asia Pacific) Limited (September 28, 2019).

As mentioned in Chapter 3, the Organization for Security and Co-operation in Europe (OSCE) recently hosted the **19th Alliance against Trafficking in Persons Conference** in Vienna, Austria, focusing on the theme of technology as a weapon that can be wielded for good or evil.[366] OSCE outlined two main goals for this two-day conference: "(1) improving understanding of how technology is being misused to facilitate trafficking so that better responses can be built, and (2) exploring how technology can be developed, harmonized and deployed to help combat all forms of trafficking." During the sessions, attendees discussed ways to improve legal and institutional frameworks through strategic uses of technology in order to break the cycle of human trafficking around the world.

It isn't exclusively about creating new technologies. As we've seen, there are over 200 tech tools currently in use to combat human trafficking, yet many of them haven't gathered much traction. Often, even the stakeholders who use these tools—victim service providers, law enforcement, businesses, and civil society advocates—don't have the technical training necessary to leverage these platforms to their fullest potential. Phil Bennett, who was a co-founding member of Tech Against Trafficking, voiced this concern: "We urgently need a collective effort to strengthen promising

---

366 "19th Alliance against Trafficking in Persons." *OSCE Events*, 2019. Organization for Security and Co-operation in Europe (September 28, 2019).

technology solutions."[367] Only when these tech tools are thoroughly incorporated into the fabric of the anti-trafficking movement will we really begin to see an impact.

At the OSCE conference, Tech Against Trafficking addressed this issue with the announcement of their new **Accelerator Program**, slated for launch in the summer of 2019.[368] With the support of large tech firms like AT&T, Microsoft, Salesforce, BT, and Nokia, they plan to come alongside other organizations and agencies to offer them the technical expertise, mentorship, and resources they need to maximize the effectiveness of the technologies.

As far as exploring new avenues for tech development, a promising strategy is to simply encourage brainstorming around this issue. Especially among the next generation of tech professionals, we're starting to see more engagement with challenges for young people to innovate solutions to human trafficking.

For instance, the non-profit organization Pasos Libres Foundation has partnered with the United Nations Office on Drugs and Crime (UNODC) and the tech giant IBM to put on an event called **BlueHack**, an initiative against human trafficking. The first hackathon of its kind—one that concentrates exclusively on creating solutions to human

---

367 "Accelerating the use of tech to combat human trafficking." *Relief-Web*, April 30, 2019. UN Office for the Coordination of Humanitarian Affairs (September 28, 2019).
368 Ibid.

trafficking—BlueHack debuted in 2018 in Bogotá, Colombia, with subsequent versions in São Paulo, Brazil, and New Jersey.[369]

BlueHack brings together university students and young technical professionals who spend thirty-two hours designing technology to address one of three challenges: (1) identify and rescue victims of human trafficking; (2) increase efficiency in the collection and management of data related to crime; and (3) strengthen efforts to prevent trafficking in the United States.[370] Throughout the event, mentors from the hackathon hosts advise each team on human trafficking, code design, and marketing strategies. This way, they can help make sure the projects are realistic and relevant to the realities of human trafficking.

Then, some of the winning entries go on to become full-fledged sponsored projects, such as a program to analyze posts and messages for indications of trafficking; a process for validating online job offers; a generated graph marking "hot spots" for exploitation zones; or a mobile app that allows victims of sex trafficking to send a request for help.

In June 2019, another collaboration between Google, the City of Austin, and a local nonprofit called **Whatever It Takes** culminated in a hackathon for high school students

369 Arevalo Sanchez, Sebastian. "OYW Ambassador hosts 1st hackathon against human trafficking in US." *One Young World Blog*, October 23, 2019. One Young World (September 28, 2019).

370 Ibid.

in Austin, Texas. This hackathon specifically called attention to the current state of domestic sex trafficking in Texas, which claims over 79,000 minors as victims. Student Cecille Archer said the hackathon was a wakeup call for her. "I didn't realize how prominent [human trafficking] is within Austin," she said. "It's devastating that people my age are going through these slavery-type situations and I'm at home, safe and sound."[371] Like the other students at the hackathon, she realized that she couldn't stand by idle while girls her age were being trafficked for sex in her own city.

In organizing this event for local youth, Whatever It Takes aimed to bring this generation to the table, inviting them into the conversation to help find solutions to this horrific problem. "They really took this passionately, they took it seriously, which I thought was phenomenal," said Sophia Strother, one of the judges and a sex trafficking survivor herself.[372] She was extremely impressed by the students' dedication, teamwork, and commitment to step up to the plate and take on the responsibility to prevent human trafficking among their peers. It wasn't just a one-day initiative. She could see that their fire will continue to blaze for years to come.

This is why I'm hopeful!

---

371 Falcon, Russell. "Youth Hackathon tackles human trafficking with City of Austin." *KXAN News*, June 9, 2019. Nexstar Broadcasting, Inc. (September 28, 2019).

372 Ibid.

CADEN'S STORY

It was a sultry afternoon in August 2018 when seventeen-year-old Caden Moskowitz and his dad disembarked from a tuk-tuk at the entrance to an office building in Bangkok, Thailand. "We almost crashed, like, three times on the way there, the drivers were crazy," he remembered. Bangkok is a "really intimidating place to just step into and try to travel around, even if you travel a lot." And as far as traveling goes, Caden was no newbie: every summer, he and his family journeyed around the world, experiencing other cultures.

"We got to the office building, not really sure if we're in the right place, go up the elevator," he told me, reliving that day. Eventually, he and his dad found the room where Dorna Sukkree and two of her partners stood up to greet them. A lawyer and the executive director of the Multi-stakeholders Initiative for Accountable Supply Chain of Thai Fishers (MAST), Dorna began to share how the MAST coalition was taking action to combat labor trafficking in the Thai fishing industry.

✱✱

Although I'd connected with Dorna in February 2019 to learn about MAST's partnership with Pelagic Data Systems to pilot vessel-tracking technology among small-scale fishing communities in Thailand, I didn't know about Caden until the final few weeks of writing this manuscript, when I received an update from Dorna about her work. In her email, she briefly mentioned a teenager who was helping MAST with the development of an app designed to gather human intelligence from fishermen.

My immediate thought: *I have to talk with this guy.*

When I asked her about it, Dorna was kind enough to put us in touch, and after a few scheduling mishaps—Caden had just jumped into the craziness of college at the University of Berkeley, California, while I was studying abroad in Rome— we finally jumped onto a FaceTime call.

"Hey!" Caden appeared on the screen, headphones around his neck and a smile on his face. With the sounds of dogs and college students in the background, we chatted for an hour before he had to run to his next class. During our conversation, I realized that Caden embodies so much of what I've striven to cover in this book. He exudes a casual confidence that invites others irresistibly into his enthusiasm, from his heart for combating human trafficking to his passion for down-to-earth, data-driven solutions.

His story begins the summer before his senior year of high school.

"I was just reading *The Economist* one day, and I read about MAST, and that's kind of how everything started," he began. "I was really inspired by [Dorna and everything she's doing]." Since his family had already planned a trip to Thailand that year, he decided to reach out to see if he could learn more about her work and help her in any way. A couple emails later, he found himself anticipating a meeting with Dorna in person, something he had never done before during his travels abroad. He was about to embark on an unforgettable journey.

Caden saw the plight of fishermen in Southeast Asia, and he couldn't turn away. In Thailand, he witnessed fish sold for way cheaper than it should be—it might seem like a good deal, but underneath the surface these low prices signal injustice. "If you're a human trafficker selling fish versus honest fishermen, who can sell the fish for less? The human traffickers," Caden explained. "So they're undercutting all these fishermen and it's hurting the economy... honest fishermen are forced to either quit their jobs and they're not able to support their family, or [they have to resort to] terrible things like human trafficking. It's almost like an ongoing disease that is plaguing Thailand." During his time in Bangkok, Caden would walk around the ports and see people hustling for money in congested streets, struggling to make ends meet. "It was sad to see," he said.

From there, Caden began reading more about human trafficking, growing ever more appalled at the current situation and even more so at how little was being done about it. His own life felt increasingly lucky: "We are such privileged kids...I go to a great school, I went to a great high school." That gratefulness only exacerbated his frustration that very few people leverage their privileged positions to help those in need. According to Caden, "Right now in Thailand, there are 610,000 people currently living in conditions of modern slavery… there are 1.2 million people in Indonesia, 575,000 in Myanmar, 261,000 in Cambodia… And that's just not right. It shouldn't be like that."[373] And yet, so many people don't know that slavery still exists. "Why is nobody talking about this? Why isn't everybody here, working to solve this issue? It's *slavery*."

Caden was prepared to help however he could, and he found a need that could be filled with technology. "I just wanted to find anything I could do to help these people thrive and help [improve] their economy and government. I went into [the meeting with Dorna] thinking, I'm going to do one thing for her. I'm going to do whatever I can to help." During their meeting, he sat down with his father as Dorna and two of her MAST partners explained more details about their work. They brainstormed through some of the challenges they faced, taking notes and discussing possible ways that Caden could get involved.

After talking with Dorna, Caden distinctly remembers, "Her main takeaway from the entire meeting was this set of words that I said: *human intelligence*." In order to tackle human trafficking on a comprehensive level, they needed to gather intelligence from the entire community, from individual people—"eyes that are watching." Currently, one of the barriers to effective anti-slavery work is that "everything is kind of ambiguous and a little bit unknown," Caden

---

373 "2018 Findings: Executive Summary." *Global Slavery Index*, 2018. The Walk Free Foundation (September 28, 2019).

explained, with information varying from website to website. "It's really hard to track something that is illegal, unregulated, and unreported, like human trafficking." But he—and Dorna—believed that there was incredible power in data. With the right technology, MAST could harness massive amounts of information from the thousands of employees on Thai fishing vessels, gathering insights for prevention, intervention, and the empowerment of fishermen against labor abuses.

"I started realizing that I could fill that gap for them [with technology]," Caden told me. "I didn't necessarily [think] that that's what we were going to do. I honestly was just going to the meeting to see how I could help her." And the solution turned out to be facilitated by technology, which was a perfect fit for Caden. Already involved with The App Company, a small enterprise managed by his serial entrepreneur father, he seized the opportunity to lead this app development project. His goal: to collect more data for MAST so that they could analyze the current state of human trafficking on Thai fishing vessels, perform predictive behavior analysis to prevent conditions that allow for exploitation, and provide fishermen with a tool to report unsafe conditions and join forces against abuse. It would be a way for "each person to be collecting data and have technology in their hands."

After his trip to Thailand, Caden familiarized himself with Java and HTML, wanting a more realistic understanding of how apps are built and how features like buttons or drop-down menus are implemented. He and his father mobilized The App Company's programming teams to work on this project, and Caden's been involved ever since. "I'm versed enough to be able to communicate with programmers," he told me. As a student pursuing the field of Business Administration and Management, he doesn't actually do any of the coding himself. Instead, he acts as a manager, testing prototypes of the app and giving directions to the programmers. He'll let them know if a button isn't working or if there's an idea he wants to implement, such as adding a map button in the top right corner of the interface. He's also in regular communication with Dorna, talking with her about once a week to make sure that everything is unfolding in a timely and user-informed manner.

Caden designed this technology, the MAST Human Intelligence App, keeping the users front and center. During our FaceTime conversation, he pulled up the app on his phone and listed off the features for me. "Our first idea was, okay, let's have a panic button. Obviously, it's evolved immensely since then." When someone downloads the app, they first set up a worker profile with their name, height, weight, eye color, date of birth, and government ID number; a place to link social media accounts including Facebook, Twitter, Instagram, WeChat, and WhatsApp; and emergency contact numbers of family and friends. This way, if a worker goes missing, MAST and The App Company will have plenty of details to aid in finding them. When pressed, the app's panic button sends an alert to the user's emergency contacts; in addition, a witness button will automatically record fifteen seconds of audio that is then sent to MAST. Users can also submit a witness report to document "red flags" that they may observe aboard a fishing vessel, such as physical abuse; intimidating behavior, a dock worker who never signed a contract to work at sea; workers under sixteen years of age; retention of identity documents; withholding of wages; or illegalities regarding crew size, fishing gear, or the amount of fish caught.

All these data points are then organized on a map where MAST will be able to see trends and hone in on areas where they might need to investigate. For example, if twenty workers reported unsafe conditions for the same vessel ID number that year, or if the panic signal was pressed multiple times by different users in the same region, MAST might want to look into the possibility of labor abuses aboard that boat. "Once we have the app up and running, and fishermen are using it and downloading it in these certain places, we'll *know*," Caden told me, the excitement evident in his face. "We'll be able to see what's going on, and it will paint a very clear picture of areas that are in high demand for needing help."

The app doesn't just empower the MAST coalition; it also contains a community section where fishermen can reach out to other workers, whether they're on the same boat or located miles away. Through a chat tool, they are able to support each other as part of a greater network. They can also rate vessel

ID numbers to warn others of boats that they've deemed unsafe. When inputting a vessel into their work log, other users will be able to see those ratings and protect themselves from entering potentially dangerous situations. It's fishermen helping other fishermen—I can't think of a better solution.

I was blown away as Caden described feature after feature of the MAST Human Intelligence App. It's truly a comprehensive tool! **And he makes sure that the people who will be using the app will have the technical infrastructure necessary for it to be effective.**

It was something I'd been wondering about, so I asked, "Do most of the fishermen have some sort of device that they could download the app onto?"

Caden grinned. "If the answer to that was no, that would be bad. Luckily, it's yes." He explained that the Labor Rights Promotion Network, which had partnered with Dorna to launch MAST in 2016, has ensured that hundreds of thousands of fishermen across Thailand have Samsung phones. What an incredible initiative!

Caden is also mindful of issues like Wi-Fi availability; out at sea, some features might not be an option. "You're probably thinking, you need Wi-Fi to press a panic button, right?" he said, anticipating my next question. How are you going to send a signal when you're far from shore with no service? To solve that problem, the app offers something called an "active job." Users can create an active job before leaving the port, where they enter details about the job description; their employee contract; vessel ID; and port, date, and time for both embarking and disembarking the vessel. If a fisherman doesn't check back into the app a few hours after he planned to return, Caden explained that the app "will automatically activate the panic button for you through the account and notify all of your emergency contacts that you're in some sort of danger and show your last position." It's like having an extra pair of eyes watching over their safety.

Soon, Caden will be planning an in-person training to teach fishermen how to utilize all the features of the app. He's also working on making the platform accessible in multiple languages—Thai, Burmese, and Cambodian to start—as well as designing the visual interface so that even someone who can't read will still be able to figure out the app. He can't wait to be back in Southeast Asia to interact with the local fishermen. "It's customers, customers, customers"—that's the focus. "You don't know what they need until you ask them." Their feedback is invaluable for making the app the best it can be.

But Caden doesn't stop there. **He's doing everything he can to bring others into his mission.** He told me that in the next year, he's hoping to mobilize a team of ambitious individuals to help him with the training and deployment of the app in Thailand. They have to not only be passionate about the project like he is but also flexible and hard-working, willing to put in the effort to make it successful. Together, they will "start interacting with the people that will be using the app and teaching them how to use it and getting their feedback."

He doesn't want to do this alone. As a drummer in several bands, Caden couldn't resist using a music analogy to illustrate his perspective on collaboration. "What I've learned is, the more people you include, the more diversity of sound your music has," he told me. "And that's what I want to do with my business and my ideas, get everyone involved that wants to help me, and include everybody, as long as they're working on it as hard as I am. I'm able to develop and make so much more because of that." I think he phrased it beautifully.

On the brink of deployment, Caden is determined to take this idea all the way to an unimaginable impact. "I'm so excited to see how [the app] works with Thai fishermen," he said, adding that "we probably chose one of the hardest things to do first, honestly." Regarding human intelligence, he believes that this type of app can be applied to other exploitation-prone scenarios for a safer world all around. "That's how these great ideas start," he reflected. "Starting very small, specific... if we can do it with Thai fishermen, we can do it with people traveling, we can do it with people backpacking..." Even parents who send their children on airplane flights by themselves could benefit from this kind of app to make sure that they can take action right away if something goes wrong.

Through it all, Caden has been the driver of this entire project. "Right now it's kind of jumbled because I just left for college," he told me, a bit regretfully. "It's been busy with school and everything, but things don't get done when I'm not there." Although the programmers are constantly working on updates, he's really the one providing the vision and direction. Yet he doesn't take much credit at all. When it comes down to it, "Dorna's need for technology inspired me to use my resources and my communication skills [to] assist her." Creating the MAST Human Intelligence App is simply part of Caden's responsibility to his fellow humans, leveraging the opportunities he's been given to empower others so that they can live with the same freedom and dignity.

All of this on top of a full-time college workload, musical commitments, and other social entrepreneurship ventures?

It's insanely inspiring.

STAND UP

What about you? Maybe this book has stirred you to learn more about how you can use technology to fight human trafficking—I hope it has.

I've long discarded the naive notion that technology can "save the day." It's a powerful tool, but it's not the silver bullet. Even the most sophisticated software will fail to make an impact unless we really understand what's happening on the ground and how technology should be integrated with current initiatives… which means that close communication with other sectors is absolutely critical.

So it's not the end-all-be-all. Still, I don't believe we can dismantle this widespread crime *without* technology. We must leverage it to our advantage.

If you're studying computer science or already working in the tech industry, I want to challenge you to consider ways to give back toward this cause. Hackathons, internships, and independent projects are some ways to help brainstorm innovative anti-trafficking solutions. Volunteering your technical skills for a nonprofit organization is also extremely valuable.

Keep in mind that, when it comes to aligning your expertise with a stakeholder's needs, you might have to learn some new skills or be willing to help out in less prominent ways. Maybe, like Caden, you'll need to familiarize yourself with coding so that you can understand what's realistic when developing an app. Perhaps, like Christine Chen, you'll be most useful to an organization by making phone calls to find a technology platform that fits their most pressing needs. Or like me, you might need to gain more experience in data science and machine learning before you'll be ready to contribute in a fully technical role. But that doesn't mean that you can't get involved in another capacity. No matter what your contributions look like, the anti-trafficking world could definitely use you!

Maybe you're not a software developer, but you can still contribute in many ways. You can download an app like TraffickCam or participate in the University of Nottingham's Slavery from Space project to add to national datasets. You can volunteer at victim service shelters to get hands-on experience with the challenges these individuals face. You can help to cover the cost of computers for survivor-driven companies such as Starfish Project. You can be conscious of the products you purchase and the companies you support. You can warn your young friends to be wary of online strangers or hand a helpline text number to someone you suspect might be caught in unwilling work.

Above all, I want you to know that a major career shift isn't the only way to help fight human trafficking. It's okay to enjoy your job and find fulfillment in your current projects, whatever they might be. And it's wonderful if you're involved in another "tech for good" cause that inspires you. Anti-trafficking is not the only movement you can conscientiously support—you can be an advocate regardless of your other employment or volunteer commitments. At your day job, sparking change can be as simple as bringing up the issue in the staff lounge, keeping your coworkers accountable for the online sites they're searching, investigating your company's policies regarding supply chain transparency, and making sure your products are ethically sourced. In fact, perhaps we don't need thousands of people to drop their jobs for full-time anti-slavery work, so much as we need everyone, wherever they are, to initiate the changes in our social priorities and business practices that we'll need in order to combat human trafficking at a systemic level.

Whether you're a technologist or not, I hope you've seen that somewhere, somehow, there is something you can do to stand up for freedom. In one way or another, we all can play a part in abolishing modern-day slavery. From the products we consume to the conversations we initiate among our friends and families, it's the small changes that will end up making a collective impact.

As Princess Eugenie phrased it: "We stand for all the people that cannot stand here today."[374]

Let's stand up for those who don't yet have the freedom we enjoy.

---

374 "Using technology to combat trafficking in human beings: OSCE Alliance against Trafficking conference explores how to turn a liability into an asset." *OSCE Newsroom*, April 9, 2019. Organization for Security and Co-operation in Europe (September 28, 2019).

ACKNOWLEDGMENTS

All thanks be to the Lord, my Savior and Sustainer, the One who sets the captives free. *"But let justice run down like water, and righteousness like a mighty stream."*—Amos 5:24

I'm so grateful for my family who supported me every step of the way. Dad, thank you for giving me the thumbs up to dive into this project, that night I was too scared to start on my own. Mom, thank you for sharing my excitement and bearing my burdens. Jessica, Abel, Kaley, Nathanael, Elette, and Gideon—y'all brought so much joy to the journey.

Thank you to all my interviewees. It means so much that you would take time out of your busy schedules to share your stories with me. Your passion inspires me daily.

Christine, Evangeline, and Vanessa—thank you for allowing me to share my hopes and doubts with you throughout the writing process. A special shoutout to Michelle who never complained despite my late nights and early mornings, and often surprised me with sticky notes of encouragement on my desk.

I can't thank my team at New Degree Press enough, especially Eric Koester, Brian Bies, Shelby Hogan, and Elina Oliferovskiy, for cheering me on and believing in me when I wasn't sure I could do it. And to my fellow authors, Aviva and Eun Hye, we made it!

Lastly, a tremendous appreciation for everyone who pre-ordered the eBook or paperback to make this publication possible. Thank you for spreading the news about *Data for Dignity*, providing feedback on my manuscript, and helping me launch these words into the world.

Vimarys Alverio	Kendall Foley
Robert Beiser*	Ray Fung
Adam Birchfield	Ted and Lucibeth Hamm
Jerry and Jackie Birchfield+	Gladys Hitt
Pam Birchfield	Anna Hyde
Henie Brandol	Neeraj K. Kanhere
Andrey Butenko	Daniel Kim
Deanna Carter	Jill L. Kostomay
Lauren Chang	Joshua Lansing
Jeremy and Jocelyn Chen	Eunia Lee
Eric Dalke	Jordon Lewis
Mikylla Davy	Vanessa Lim
Karen Edwards	Shin-Lien Lin+

Sara Loudon[+]

Callie Ann Lum

Jessie Ma

Nathan Maris

David Miyatake

Caden Moskowitz[*]

Giao Nguyen

Catherine Stoddard Pollock

Alyson Robbins

Liz Rush[*]

Tammy Senior

Gabriel Spearin[+]

Hayden Stockwell[+]

Victoria Teng

Thyda Tsai

Ted Way

Cameron Wong

Sophie Ye

Jessica Zhu

Triona Anderson

Eden Berga

Danielle Birchfield

Jessica Birchfield

Stan and MeMe Birchfield[+]

Amity Buckner

Ali Byott

Rachel Cash

Vivien K. Chang

Christine Chen[*]

Andy Davidson[+]

Hector Dominguez-Maceda

Aimee Ellis

Chloe Fong

Connor Geiman

Andrea Hattler Bramson

Dedra Hopper

Emily Iversen

Maura Keith

Alexandra Klezovich

Jordan Kussman

Sonya Lao

Alvina Leung[+]

Millicent Li

Elizabeth Lin

William Locatelli

Andrea Lum

Taryn Lum

Ben MacMillan

Rachel McAmis

Vicki Miyatake

Wesley Muthemba

Angela Phillips

Peter Reinhardt

Rachel Rodney

Suja Santiago

Diljit S. Sethi[+]

Sammi St. Arnold

Dornnapha Sukkree[*]

Joanne Toll
Justin Underwood*
Steven and Sunny Wei+
Judah Wylie
Ian Yeo
Susan Bean+
Danyel Bigger
Denise Birchfield
Logan Birchfield+
Kyle Bishop+
Joan Burdon
Heather Carlson
Winston Chan
Shirley Chang
Matthew Cho-Lew
DeFord Davis+
Arthur Dyachk
Christine Everson
Geoff Freeman*
Spencer Reese Giles
Paul Heffner
Vivian Hua
Renate Kaelin
Laurie Ketron
Eric Koester

Courtney Kwan
Srinithi Latha
Stacy Lew
Jenny Liang
Michelle Lin
Jacquelynn Loos*
Katie Lum
Joseph Lum+
Daniel Mar+
Elizabeth McInnis
Ivan Montero
Staci Nelson
Corbin Phipps
Joanna Rives
Horacio Roman-Gomez
Evangeline J. Schmitt
Amy Shan
Colby Steich
Calob Symonds+
Chrissy Tsai
Emilia Vanderwerf*
Vera Wong
Michele Yamashita
Elaine Yu+

Key: *featured interviewee, +special contribution

APPENDIX

———

INTRODUCTION

"2018 Findings: Executive Summary." *Global Slavery Index*, 2018. The Walk Free Foundation (September 28, 2019).

"Fact Sheet: Human Trafficking." *Office on Trafficking in Persons*, November 21, 2017. U.S. Department of Health & Human Services (September 28, 2019).

CHAPTER 1

"2018 Findings: Executive Summary." *Global Slavery Index*, 2018. The Walk Free Foundation (September 28, 2019).

Andrews, Frank. "The Paris park where Nigerian women and forced into prostitution." *The CNN Freedom Project*, October 5, 2018. CNN (September 28, 2019).

"#Envision2030 Goal 8: Decent Work and Economic Growth." *United Nations Department of Economic and Social Affairs*, 2016. United Nations (September 28, 2019).

Gehr, Danielle. "Newspaper carrier picked up sex-trafficking victim, leading to Illinois woman's arrest." *Des Moines Register*, August 2, 2019. Des Moines Register (September 28, 2019).

"Global Estimates of Modern Slavery. *International Labour Office*, 2017. International Labour Organization, Walk Free Foundation, and International Organization for Migration (September 28, 2019).

"How many slaves work for you?." *Slavery Footprint*, 2011. Made in a Free World (September 28, 2019).

"ILO says forced labour generates annual profits of US$ 150 billion." *ILO*, May 20, 2014. International Labour Organization (September 28, 2019).

Jardine, Akilah. "Labour Exploitation in the UK's Hand Car Wash Sector." *Delta 8.7*, August 14, 2019. United Nations University Centre for Policy Research to Alliance 8.7 (September 28, 2019).

Johansen, Raggie. "Child trafficking in Ghana." *UNODC*, 2019, United Nations Office on Drugs and Crime (September 28, 2019).

"Millenium Declaration." un.org, September 2000. United Nations (September 28, 2019).

"One Hundred Sixth Congress of the United States of America at the Second Session." *Gov Info*, January 24, 2000. U.S. Government Publishing Office (September 28, 2019).

"Orphanage 'recruited kids to get donations'." *The CNN Freedom Project*, March 8, 2017. CNN (September 28, 2019).

"Protocol to Prevent, Suppress and Punish Trafficking in Persons Especially Women and Children, supplementing the United Nations Convention against Transnational Organized Crime."

United Nations Human Rights Office of the High Commissioner,
November 15, 2000. United Nations (September 28, 2019).

Richmond, John. "Taking a Lesson From Traffickers: Harness-
ing Technology To Further the Anti-Trafficking Movement's
Principal Goals." *U.S. Mission to the OSCE,* April 8, 2019. U.S.
Mission to the OSCE (September 28, 2019).

Romo, Rafael. "Thirty years living and working as a modern-day
slave." *The CNN Freedom Project,* April 28, 2017. CNN (September 28, 2019).

"Six teens rescued during FBI sex trafficking sweep in Seattle."
Komo News, August 7, 2019. Sinclair Broadcast Group (September 28, 2019).

Soares, Isa. "These men were forced into slavery in Scotland." *The
CNN Freedom Project,* 2017. CNN (September 28, 2019).

"Survivor overcomes her sex trafficking past." *The CNN Freedom
Project,* 2017. CNN (September 28, 2019).

"Trafficking in Persons Report." *State.gov,* June 24, 2019. U.S.
Department of State (September 28, 2019).

"United Nations Convention against Transnational Organized
Crime and the Protocols Thereto." *United Nations Office on
Drugs and Crime,* 2004. United Nations (September 28, 2019).

CHAPTER 2

"3Ps: Prosecution, Protection, and Prevention." *Office to Monitor
and Combat Trafficking in Persons,* 2019. U.S. Department of
State (September 28, 2019).

Andrews, Jordan. "Reducing Exploitation of Migrant Workers via
the Blockchain—Handshake.tech." *Hackernoon,* September 24,
2017. Hackernoon (September 28, 2019).

Bennett, Phil. "A new chapter in my career - let's tackle modern slavery." *Pulse*, October 18, 2018. LinkedIn (September 8, 2019).

Bennett, Phil. "Inspired by the Cause: Using Technology to Fight Human Trafficking—a Pro bono Story." *Salesforce Blog*, January 19, 2017. Salesforce (September 28, 2019).

Guilbert, Kieran. "UK royal, US ambassador tout tech tools to tackle human trafficking." *Reuters News Trust*, April 8, 2019. Thomson Reuters Foundation (September 28, 2019).

Jha, Monica. "The Dark Hand of Tech that Stokes Sex Trafficking in India." *Factor Daily*, February 25, 2019. Sourcecode Media (August 20, 2019).

Richmond, John. "Taking a Lesson From Traffickers: Harnessing Technology To Further he Anti-Trafficking Movement's Principal Goals." *U.S. Mission to the OSCE*, April 8, 2019. U.S. Mission to the OSCE (September 28, 2019).

"Using technology to combat trafficking in human beings: OSCE Alliance against Trafficking conference explores how to turn a liability into an asset." *OSCE Newsroom*, April 9, 2019. Organization for Security and Co-operation in Europe (September 28, 2019).

CHAPTER 3

"Ashton Kutcher on Using the Power of Technology for Good." *YouTube*, January 12, 2018. Salesforce Events & Dreamforce (September 28. 2019).

Bennett, Phil. "A new chapter in my career - let's tackle modern slavery." *Pulse*, October 18, 2018. LinkedIn (September 8, 2019).

Drejer, Catharina. "«Tech for good» på sårbares bekostning [at the expense of the vulnerable]." *Skaperkraft*, January 25, 2019. Tankesmien Skaperkraft (September 28, 2019; translation).

Richmond, John. "Taking a Lesson From Traffickers: Harnessing Technology To Further he Anti-Trafficking Movement's Principal Goals." *U.S. Mission to the OSCE*, April 8, 2019. U.S. Mission to the OSCE (September 28, 2019).

CHAPTER 4

"2019 Trafficking in Persons Report." *State.gov*, June 2019. United States Department of State (September 28, 2019).

"Activism 2.0: Coding against sex trafficking." *Berkeley News*, January 30, 2019. University of California, Berkeley (September 28, 2019).

"Ashton Kutcher Speech on Human Trafficking Before Congress." *YouTube*, February 15, 2017. ABC News (September 28, 2019).

Beaumont, Peter. "Experts reach for the stars to fight slavery as satellite pictures tell all." *The Guardian*, March 19, 2018. Guardian News & Media Limited (September 28, 2019).

Davis, Matt. "One-third of all slavery is visible from space." *Big Think*, February 22, 2019. Big Think Edge (September 28, 2019).

"Fighting slavery from space." *Vision*, no. 03 (2019). University of Nottingham (September 28, 2019).

Guilbert, Kieran. "Satellites and science turn tide in fight to end slavery: expert." *Reuters*, November 15, 2017. Thomson Reuters Foundation (September 28, 2019).

"India: debt bondage." *Anti-Slavery*, 2019. Anti-Slavery International (September 28, 2019).

Jackson, Bethany. "Slavery from Space: A Remote Sensing Approach to Ending Modern Slavery." *Delta 8.7*, March 7, 2019.

United Nations University Centre for Policy Research to Alliance 8.7 (September 28, 2019).

Magee, Tamlin. "Inside GEN, the nonprofit combatting human trafficking with big data." *Computerworld*, January 11, 2019. IDG Communications (September 28, 2019).

McDonald, Claire. "Machine data for good: How Splunk is partnering with firms to make the world a better place." *Computer Weekly*, November 16, 2017. TechTarget (September 28, 2019).

McGoogan, Cara and Muktadir Rashid. "Satellites reveal 'child slave camps' in Unesco-protected park in Bangladesh." *The Telegraph*, October 23, 2016. Telegraph Media Group (September 28, 2019).

Mitra, Dakhina and Delphine Valette. "Brick by Brick: Environment, Human Labour & Animal Welfare." *The Brooke*, 2017. International Labour Organization, The Brooke Hospital for Animals, and The Donkey Sanctuary (September 28, 2019).

New, Joshua. "5 Q's for Sherrie Caltagirone, Executive Director of the Global Emancipation Network." *Data Innovation*, November 5, 2018. Center for Data Innovation, (September 28, 2019).

O'Brien, Sara Ashley. "Ashton Kutcher's nonprofit gets boost to fight against child abuse on the internet." *CNN Business*, April 17, 2019. CNN (September 28, 2019).

Ounsworth, Rob. "Professor Kevin Bales; how science can help end slavery." *University of Nottingham Blog*, February 3, 2017. University of Nottingham (September 28, 2019).

Reynolds, Matt. "Volunteers teach AI to spot slavery sites from satellite images." *NewScientist*, June 23, 2017. New Scientist (September 28, 2019).

Scoles, Sarah. "Researchers spy signs of slavery from space." *Science Mag*, February 19, 2019. American Association for the Advancement of Science (September 28, 2019).

Seelochan, Isaac. "New university project aiming to end slavery—from space." *Notts TV*, July 4, 2017. Notts TV (September 28, 2019).

"Slavery From Space." *Zooniverse*, 2017. University of Nottingham Rights Lab (September 28, 2019).

"Spotlight Changes the Way Law Enforcement Investigates Sex Trafficking." *Spotlight*, 2019. Thorn and Digital Reasoning (September 28, 2019).

"theCube Interview with Sherrie Caltagirone." *Global Emancipation NGO*, September 26, 2017. Global Emancipation Network (September 28, 2019).

Thorpe, Devin. "The New Sheriff In Human Trafficking Is Wielding Big Data." *Forbes*, October 11, 2018. Forbes Media (September 28, 2019).

Vomiero, Jessica. "U.K. researchers use Google satellite images to identify signs of slavery in India." *Global News*, August 6, 2017. Corus Entertainment (September 28, 2019).

Wardlaw, Jessica. "Slavery from Space: Citizen Science in the Antislavery Movement." *SciStarter*, April 6, 2019. Arizona State University and the National Science Foundation (September 28, 2019).

"We are Thorn." *YouTube*, November 14, 2013. Thorn (September 28, 2019).

Woods, Kyle and Kyle Hartsock. "Using Spotlight to investigate human trafficking." *Thorn Blog*, August 9, 2018. Thorn (September 28, 2019).

CHAPTER 5

"2018 Findings: Fishing." *Global Slavery Index*, 2018. The Walk Free Foundation (September 28, 2019).

"About Phone Story." *Phone Story,* 2019. Molleindustria (September 28, 2019).

Brettmann, Mar and Sandip Soli. "Sex Trafficking is Bad For Businesses." *BEST Alliance,* September 10, 2015. Businesses Ending Slavery & Trafficking (September 28, 2019).

Dredge, Stuart. "Apple bans satirical iPhone game Phone Story from its App Store." *The Guardian,* September 14, 2011. Guardian News & Media Limited (September 28, 2019).

Drejer, Catharina. "«Tech for good» på sårbares bekostning [at the expense of the vulnerable]." *Skaperkraft,* January 25, 2019. Tankesmien Skaperkraft (September 28, 2019; translation).

"Fair Trade Standards." *Fair Trade Certified,* 2019. Fair Trade USA (September 28, 2019).

Garren, Melissa. "Technology to Fill Data Gaps at Sea." *International Conservation,* September 14, 2016. International Conservation Caucus Foundation (September 28, 2019).

Hick, Melanie. "Apple Bans Anti-iPhone Game App." *Huffington Post,* November 14, 2011. Verizon Media (September 28, 2019).

Holbrook, Angie. "Angie Holbrook: Why I fundraise for Thorn." *Thorn Blog,* November 8, 2018. Thorn (September 28, 2019).

"How Demand Impacts Human Trafficking Statistics on a Global Scale." *USC Suzanne Dowark-Peck News,* January 18, 2019. USC Suzanne Dworak-Peck School of Social Work (September 28, 2019).

"MAST Human: A Nonprofit Combating Human Trafficking at Seas." *MAST Human* (September 28, 2019).

Mirfendereski, Taylor. "Seattle nonprofit takes on sex buyers with technology." *K5 News,* November 8, 2017. KING-TV (September 28, 2019).

"NatGeo Marine Protection Prize Press Release." *Pelagic Data,* June 8, 2018. Pelagic Data Systems (September 28, 2019).

Rosoff, Henry. "Using memes, Facebook videos and Google adds to combat sex trafficking." *KIRO 7*, April 12, 2017. Cox Media Group (September 28, 2019).

"Thailand: Forced Labor, Trafficking Persist in Fishing Fleets." *Human Rights Watch News*, January 23, 2018. Human Rights Watch (September 28, 2019).

"Thailand: Forced Labor, Trafficking Persist in Fishing Fleets." *YouTube*, January 22, 2018. Human Rights Watch (September 28, 2019).

"We are Thorn." *YouTube*, November 14, 2013. Thorn (September 28, 2019).

"Why Focus On Sex Buyers?." *YouTube*, September 19, 2017. KING 5 News (September 28, 2019).

Wortham, Jenna. "Game That Critiques Apple Vanishes From App Store." *Bits*, September 13, 2011. The New York Times Company (September 28, 2019).

Yi, Beh Lih and Rina Chandran. "Thailand banks on tech to end slavery at sea as workers push for rights." *Reuters*, June 19, 2018. Thomson Reuters Foundation (September 28, 2019).

CHAPTER 6

Drejer, Catharina. "Blockchain-teknologi kan brukes mot slaveri. Men vi kjenner ikke alle konsekvensene [Blockchain technology can be used against slavery. But we do not know all the consequences]." *Skaperkraft*, November 19, 2018. Tankesmien Skaperkraft (September 28, 2019; translation).

Lee, Dave. "The chatbot taking on Seattle's sex trade." *BBC News*, November 25, 2017. BBC (September 28, 2019).

"National Human Trafficking Hotline." *Polaris Project*, 2019. Polaris (September 28, 2019).

"OFW Watch." Mynd Dynamic Team (September 28, 2019).

"Our Programs: Community Advocacy." *I Want Rest*, 2019. Real Escape from the Sex Trade (September 28, 2019).

"Our Programs: REST Principles of Care." *I Want Rest*, 2019. Real Escape from the Sex Trade (September 28, 2019).

Padillo, Maya. "OFW Watch app ready for download." *Business World*, February 5, 2018. Business World Publishing (September 28, 2019).

"REST Survivors." Real Escape from the Sex Trade (September 28, 2019).

Sorsano, Freda Mae. "Former HK domestic worker develops app for OFWs." *Rappler*, October 25, 2014. Rappler (September 28, 2019).

"'The World's Terrible Truths are Never Solved by Turning a Blind Eye,' & Other Important Lessons Learned at Microsoft's 2016 // oneweek Hackathon." *I Want Rest Blog*, October 17, 2016. Real Escape from the Sex Trade (September 28, 2019).

"We are Thorn." *YouTube*, November 14, 2013. Thorn (September 28, 2019).

"We've Begun Our Year with a Real Game Changer." *REST News*, October 9, 2016. Real Escape from the Sex Trade (September 28, 2019).

"When They Go Back to the Streets, So Do We." *I Want Rest Blog*, October 23, 2018. Real Escape from the Sex Trade (September 28, 2019).

CHAPTER 7

"About Catie." *Catie Hart*, 2017. Catie Hart (September 28, 2019).

Aguilera, Diana. "Human Rights at Home: How two alums are confronting slavery in their backyard." *Stanford Magazine*, September 6, 2017. Medium (September 28, 2018).

Andrews, Frank. "The Paris park where Nigerian women and forced into prostitution." *The CNN Freedom Project*, October 5, 2018. CNN (September 28, 2019).

Beer, Kieran. "Giving Victims of Sex Trafficking Their Due." *ACAMS Today*, March 28, 2019. Association of Certified Anti-Money Laundering Specialists (September 28, 2019).

"Causes: AnnieCannons." *Charity Matters*, November 16, 2017. Charity Matters (September 28, 2019).

"Chang Chang: My Story of Hope." *Starfish Project*, 2019. Starfish Project (September 28, 2019).

Connel, Joanie. "Turning Tragedy into REAL Life: Empowering Survivors of Human Trafficking." Women Lead Radio, August 21, 2017. Connected Women of Influence (September 28, 2019).

Culp, Alice. "Starfish Project offers hope and redemption to exploited women." *South Bend Tribune*, July 24, 2016. Gate-House Media (September 28, 2019).

"Educate Her: Lay Lay." *Starfish Project*, October 30, 2018. Starfish Project (September 28, 2019).

"Episode 5—From Trafficked to Transformed: Jenny McGee of the Starfish Project." *Jessica Honegger*, February 28, 2018. Jessica Honegger (September 28, 2019).

"Fay: My Story of Hope." *Starfish Project*, 2019. Starfish Project (September 28, 2019).

Hepburn, Stephanie. "AnnieCannons is Helping Human Trafficking Survivors Become Tech Experts." *Huffington Post,* October 19, 2017. Verizon Media (September 28, 2019).

Hubley, Jessica. "Why the name 'AnnieCannons'?." *YouTube*, November 25, 2018. AnnieCannons (September 28, 2019).

Jennings, Cheryl. "Beyond the Headlines: Human Trafficking." *ABC 7 News*, December 16, 2014. ABC, Inc. (September 28, 2019).

"Lightning Talk with AnnieCannons (Jessica Hubley and Laura Hackney." *YouTube*, March 18, 2016. SFHTML5 (September 28, 2019).

McGee, Jenny. "Behind the Scenes: 12 years old." Starfish Project, March 19, 2019. Starfish Project (September 28, 2018).

"Meet Virginia Hawkins, Chief Strategy Officer at Starfish Project." *Starfish Project*, October 24, 2017. Starfish Project (September 28, 2019).

Nazaryan, Arthur. "This sex trafficking survivor is moving on—by learning how to code." *PRI GlobalPost*, August 17, 2018. Public Radio International (September 28, 2019).

"Pitching Their Stories: AnnieCannons." *YouTube*, November 9, 2017. Solve—MIT (September 28, 2019).

Romo, Rafael. "Thirty years living and working as a modern-day slave." *The CNN Freedom Project*, April 28, 2017. CNN (September 28, 2019).

Ryan, Kate. "Survivors draw on personal pasts to design anti-trafficking software." Reuters News Trust, February 21, 2019. Thomson Reuters Foundation (September 28, 2019).

"Seattle Against Slavery's Web Platform to Fight Demand." *AnnieCannons Blog*, December 19, 2018. AnnieCannons (September 28, 2019).

"Zi Yun: A Story of Hope." *YouTube*, December 30, 2016. Starfish Project (September 28, 2019).

CHAPTER 8

"British Telecommunications plc: Modern Slavery Act Transparency Statement 2017/18." *BT Digital Impact and Sustainability: Human Rights*, 2018. BT plc (September 28, 2019).

"Developing TraffickCam: Inside the Research | Washington University." *YouTube*, September 1, 2016. Washington University in St. Louis (September 28, 2019).

"Exchange Initiative: Real Resources to End Sex Trafficking." *Exchange Initiative*, 2019. Exchange Initiative (September 28, 2019).

"Fighting Crime at the Intersection of Science and Social Justice." *Institute for Public Health*, September 21, 2016. Washington University in St. Louis (September 28, 2019).

Green, Chloe. "Charity develops slavery reporting app." *Charity Digital News: Impact & Efficiency*, August 6, 2018. Charity Digital (September 28, 2019).

"How the Unseen App is Helping North Wales Police Tackle Modern Slavery." *Unseen Blog*, December 21, 2018. Unseen UK (September 28, 2019).

Jaeger, Anna and Keith Thode. "Webinar—Developing Mobile Apps from Idea to Launch: A Case Study." *YouTube*, August 23, 2013. TechSoup Global (September 28, 2019).

Kyles, Akira. "Local Organization Launches App to Keep Domestic Violence Survivors Safe." *AFRO: The Black Media Authority*, July 14, 2018. The AFRO-American Newspapers (September 28, 2019).

Martin, Allen. "Mobile App Connects Victims of Violence With Safe Spaces." *San Francisco CBS Local*, November 18, 2015. CBS Broadcasting Inc. (September 28, 2019).

Miska, Rhonda. "Q & A with Kimberly Ritter, fighting human trafficking with a smartphone app." *Global Sisters Report*, January 12, 2017. National Catholic Reporter (September 28, 2019).

"Our Impact / Modern Slavery is Real—Survivor Stories." *Unseen*, 2019. Unseen UK (September 28, 2019).

"Our People." *Unseen*, 2019. Unseen UK (September 28, 2019).

"Safe Shelter Collaborative." *Caravan Studios*, 2018. TechSoup (September 28, 2019).

Scott, Katy. "Your hotel room photos could help catch sex traffickers. *The CNN Freedom Project*, March 20, 2017. CNN Business (September 28, 2019).

Stylianou et al. "Hotels-50K: A Global Hotel Recognition Dataset." *arXiv*, January 26, 2017. Association for the Advancement of Artificial Intelligence (September 28, 2019).

"Support Unseen / Be Seen Be Heard." *Unseen*, 2018. Unseen UK (September 28, 2019).

Thomas, Emily. "Human Trafficking Survivors Find Safe Haven Through Mobile App." *Bay Area Bandwidth*, October 2, 2016. Medium (September 28, 2019).

"TraffickCam FAQ." *Exchange Initiative*, 2019. Exchange Initiative (September 28, 2019).

"Travelers use TraffickCam app to fight sex trafficking by uploading hotel room photos to national database." *Nix Assoc*, June 19, 2016. Nix Conference & Meeting Management (September 28, 2019).

"Unseen App rolled out across North Wales." *North Wales Police News and Appeals*, December 21, 2018. North Wales Police (September 28, 2019).

"Unseen Launches App to Report Modern Slavery." *Unseen News*, July 30, 2018. Unseen UK (September 28, 2019).

"Unseen, Modern Slavery Helpline: Annual Assessment 2018." *Modern Slavery Helpline*, 2018. Unseen UK and the Modern Slavery Helpline (September 28, 2019).

"Using AI To Stop Child Trafficking." *NVIDIA News Center*, February 22, 2019. NVIDIA (September 28, 2019).

Wigglesworth, Valerie. "SafeNight app comes to the aid of domestic violence victims in North Texas." *Dallas News*, October 10, 2015. The Dallas Morning News (September 28, 2019).

Wilkins, Tracee and Gina Cook. "App Helps Victims of Domestic Violence Find Safe Place to Stay." *NBC Washington*, August 15, 2018. NCB4 TV (September 28, 2019).

CHAPTER 9

"Ashton Kutcher Speech on Human Trafficking Before Congress." *YouTube*, February 15, 2017. ABC News (September 28, 2019).

Dickey, Megan Rose. "Why Google engineers worked full-time to combat sex trafficking." *TechCrunch*, January 15, 2019. Verizon Media (September 28, 2019).

Jarrett, Laura and Sara Ashley O'Brien. "Justice Department seizes classified ads website Backpage.com." *CNN Politics*, April 6, 2018. CNN (September 28, 2019).

Magee, Tamlin. "Inside GEN, the nonprofit combatting human trafficking with big data." *Computerworld*, January 11, 2019. IDG Communications (September 28, 2019).

Ricketts, Chase. "My First 30 Days as a Software Engineer at Thorn." *Thorn Blog*, October 11, 2016. Thorn (September 28, 2019).

"theCube Interview with Sherrie Caltagirone." *Global Emancipation NGO*, September 26, 2017. Global Emancipation Network (September 28, 2019).

Thorpe, Devin. "The New Sheriff In Human Trafficking Is Wielding Big Data." *Forbes*, October 11, 2018. Forbes Media (September 28, 2019).

"We are Thorn." *YouTube*, November 14, 2013. Thorn (September 28, 2019).

"When They Go Back to the Streets, So Do We." *I Want Rest Blog*, October 23, 2018. Real Escape from the Sex Trade (September 28, 2019).

CHAPTER 10

Chen et al. "Computer Security and Privacy in the Interactions Between Victim Service Providers and Human Trafficking Survivors." *28th USENIX Security Symposium*, 2019. USENIX (September 28, 2019).

"Engineering students work with Global Emancipation Network on coding project." *UP News*, March 14, 2018. University of Portland (September 28, 2019).

Ricketts, Chase. "My First 30 Days as a Software Engineer at Thorn." *Thorn Blog*, October 11, 2016. Thorn (September 28, 2019).

"STEM Education and Outreach Center Newsletter, Winter 2017 Edition." *UP STEM*, February 21, 2015. University of Portland (September 28, 2019).

"Vicarious Trauma." *Counseling Fact Sheets*, 2019. American Counseling Association (September 28, 2019).

CHAPTER 11

"19th Alliance against Trafficking in Persons." *OSCE Events*, 2019. Organization for Security and Co-operation in Europe (September 28, 2019).

"2018 Findings: Executive Summary." *Global Slavery Index*, 2018. The Walk Free Foundation (September 28, 2019).

"Accelerating the use of tech to combat human trafficking." *ReliefWeb*, April 30, 2019. UN Office for the Coordination of Humanitarian Affairs (September 28, 2019).

Arevalo Sanchez, Sebastian. "OYW Ambassador hosts 1st hackathon against human trafficking in US." *One Young World Blog*, October 23, 2019. One Young World (September 28, 2019).

Falcon, Russell. "Youth Hackathon tackles human trafficking with City of Austin." *KXAN News*, June 9, 2019. Nexstar Broadcasting, Inc. (September 28, 2019).

"Freedom Collaborative." *Liberty Shared*, 2019. Share (Asia Pacific) Limited (September 28, 2019).

"Liberty Shared: Creating an Environment Safe from Trafficking." *Liberty Shared*, 2019. Share (Asia Pacific) Limited (September 28, 2019).

Nestor, Peter, Dunstan Allison-Hope, and Hannah Darnton. "Announcing a New Collaboration Using Tech to Combat Human Trafficking." *BSR*, June 28, 2018. Business for Social Responsibility (September 28, 2019).

"Unseen Launches App to Report Modern Slavery." *Unseen News*, July 30, 2018. Unseen UK (September 28, 2019).

"Using technology to combat trafficking in human beings: OSCE Alliance against Trafficking conference explores how to turn a liability into an asset." *OSCE Newsroom*, April 9, 2019. Organization for Security and Co-operation in Europe (September 28, 2019).

"What is Delta 8.7?." *Delta 8.7*, 2019. United Nations University Centre for Policy Research to Alliance 8.7 (September 28, 2019).

Made in the USA
Coppell, TX
17 December 2019